SLIGHTLY FOXED PAPERBACKS

A LATE BEGINNER

Priscilla Napier

First published by Michael Joeseph in 1966

First published by Slightly Foxed in 2009
in a limited edition of 2,000 copies
Paperback edition 2013.

© The Estate of Priscilla Napier 1966

Slightly Foxed Ltd
53 Hoxton Square
London N1 6PB

A CIP catalogue record for this book is available from the British Library.

ISBN 978-1-906562-45-8
Printed by Smith Settle, Yeadon, West Yorkshire

Preface

The backdrop to Priscilla Napier's childhood was Egypt; the golden years of the Edwardian age were coming to an end, the First World War just around the corner, but for the confident, buoyant upper-class English of her parents' world the sun would never set upon 'the regimental band playing selections from *HMS Pinafore* under the banyan tree'. This wonderful recreation of a time and a climate of mind – a hundred years ago, one realizes, startled – is not just an evocation of place but also of the child's eye view. *A Late Beginner* ranks quite simply with the greatest accounts of how it is to be a child, to see with that strange, skewed, uncontaminated vision.

There were three children – William, Priscilla and Alethea. Their father, Sir William Hayter, was legal and financial adviser to the Egyptian government in the days of the Protectorate, a clever, hard-working man, admirably cosmopolitan in outlook and with enlightened views of the Egyptian capacity for self-rule. This was the period of nascent nationalism, the twilight of colonialism, and some, like Sir William, were preparing for it. Writing in 1966, his daughter was able to recognize his liberal outlook, while noting also that for Egypt, at least, colonial rule had not been entirely bad news, coming as it did in the wake of the considerably more brutal regime overseen by the Turks, with universal forced labour and none of the missionary zeal of the British public school administrators who saw their jobs 'as VSO or the Peace Corps might now think of them; as interesting, dangerous, ungainful and very much in the general interest'.

Priscilla's elder brother William would one day become the British Ambassador in Moscow; her younger sister Alethea would write superb books, including that innovative and seminal study of a snatch of time and a handful of people, *A Sultry Month*. Priscilla herself would marry young and lose her husband to the Second World War. But in this book William is a knickerbockered boy, packed off to prep school in England at the age of 8, and Alethea a muslin-clad toddler – all three of them under the firm rule of Nanny, who is as old as the Sphinx so far as the children are concerned but in fact, as Priscilla realizes, recalling the attentions of an Australian sergeant, 'a fair, freckled and attractive thirty-three'.

It is the recreation of people and of a vivid physical world that makes this memoir so absorbing, so immediate. The parents, kindly and devoted, the cast of Egyptian servants, the other children rampaging around the Gezira Sporting Club, with whom tribal wars are fought – Brits and Greeks and Maltese against the French, the Syrians. The garden, with its lush hot-climate vegetation and the beloved pet rabbits, and the adjacent Nile, rich with water traffic, lined with trees that are studded in the evenings with roosting egrets. The desert picnics – lightly sanded honey sandwiches supplied by 'a covey of starched nannies'. The night-time terrors: the lions that undoubtedly pace round and round the house, lean and terrible, just as seen in Cairo Zoo. Indeed yes. Oh, yes.

At this point I have to declare an interest. I too grew up in Egypt, a generation later, before and during another world war. I know about the lions. And the unremarkable presence of the Pyramids, which one never questioned because surely there was nothing unusual about a pyramid, weren't there pyramids everywhere? And one's passion for this homeland, the pride in growing up there, and the irritation of being trumped by India – 'larger, fiercer, wilder, its diseases more lethal'. For me, too, England was a far country, achieved only after a long but enthralling sea journey. And when you got there, its beaches were freezing cold and peopled with supercilious cousins. To read *A Late Beginner* is to read of my own childhood, with a few temporal adjustments (less white muslin, *Swallows and Amazons* instead of *Masterman Ready*, and Churchill a legendary figure with a cigar in his mouth instead of a rather tiresome young visiting politician whom Priscilla's father had to brief). When I came to a line in which a donkey brays with its 'sad, sobbing cry', I heard it. Not imagined – *heard*. Across time and space.

Lady Hayter took the children to England every summer, even during the first years of the war, risking possible torpedoes in the Mediterranean – Priscilla was in a state of catatonic terror. She brilliantly evokes the atmosphere of the war, the family summers at Sidmouth, doing all the ritual things but with the mothers and aunts quiet and tight-lipped with anxiety, and, by 1918, the widows everywhere, and the aunts with grim, lined faces, who would never recover from the deaths of only sons. William was by now at prep school, and did not see his father for four years; his sisters, coming to England less often, still absorbed in the carefree, hedonistic life of Cairo, seemed like strangers, though for Priscilla school was looming, England's long tentacles reaching out. There would be the train journey across the Delta, the waiting ship, the journey to a place that was not home, as there was for me.

She is an enchanting writer – sharp, shrewd, funny. The apparent artlessness of *A Late Beginner* is of course a nice deception. The book is a deft marriage of colourful observation and recall, with passages of idiosyncratic and highly intelligent reflection. She conjures up the First World War period by way of its props, the ladies' hats like 'dishes piled high with fruit and flowers and with the wings of birds'. The way in which Edwardian houses were furnished with bits of dead animals – wild buffalo horns jutting out of skulls, heads of black panthers with gleaming yellow glass eyes, the dust of the Edwardian countryside (one thinks at once of Hardy's descriptions). But she darts off also into perceptions about that time, about the nature of Englishness, about that other world that seems both yesterday and another age.

Her father was seventh out of a family of sixteen – his background that of prosperous gentry, but a family of that size at once sets them far apart from us; today such profligate fecundity would raise eyebrows at any level of society. Yet for families like this there had been a long heritage of waste – 'six out of seven family sons might be, often were, killed in foreign or civil wars, or by disease'. And Priscilla Napier proposes, with a flourish, the sustaining role of the non-celibate English clergy; 'in some Norfolk, Gloucestershire or Yorkshire rectory, Edmund, the eighth son, supplied with a modest income and supplying himself with a pretty wife, was unconcernedly chugging out a fresh set of Rogers, Henrys, Williams, Thomases, Charleses, Johns and Stephens, to be mown down, swept overboard, burnt up by Flemish or Indian fevers'.

This is the kind of memoir-writing that is invaluable social history – eye-witness stuff with the gloss of subsequent wisdoms. But to bring it off with such panache is a rare achievement. Priscilla Napier's genius is this idiosyncratic eye, an enviable turn of phrase, and an ebullient wit. The jacket photograph of the original edition shows a round-faced, slightly scowling child tricked out in white muslin, with the Sphinx and a bit of pyramid as background. Her parents are formally dressed – her mother in long skirt, high-necked blouse, wide hat, her father and a friend in jackets, ties, boater and trilby. They seem a pastiche, almost, of an unreachable period. But as soon as you start to read, everyone leaps from the page; you can hear the voices, feel their presences – and not least the presence of the plump scowling little girl, as you share her view of the bewildering and exasperating challenge of adult requirements.

Childhood is universal; circumstances may vary wildly, but the child's eye view remains very much the same – without preconceptions, without expectations, simply absorbing and recording. Priscilla Napier's eye was maverick and astute; she had the advantage of spending those crucially perceptive years in an exotic and complex country. And she was a child at the point when, as we can now see it, a particular era was coming to an end. The good fortune of her readers is that she was able to find such a beguiling and compelling voice with which to tell her story.

PENELOPE LIVELY

A LATE BEGINNER

TO WILLIAM AND ALETHEA

AUTHOR'S NOTE

'To keep a diary, or write down one's own memories at a certain age,' wrote Giuseppe di Lampedusa, 'should be a duty "State-imposed"; material thus accumulated would have inestimable value after three or four generations; many of the psychological and historical problems that assail humanity would be resolved. There are no memoirs, even those written by insignificant people, which do not include social and graphic details of first-rate importance.'

All the same, autobiography is always self-indulgent, and generally a mistake. I left Egypt in 1921 at the age of twelve and have never been back; my memory may somewhere have stumbled: I expect a few brusque letters from more mature sojourners pointing out that golden mohrs never flower until July. A number of real people who may still be living are mentioned by their real names; any resemblance between my early impressions of them, and themselves as they really were as children, will be purely coincidental.

Rockingham, 1964

I

One of the day nursery windows faced south-west across the Nile, over fields of sugar-cane and berseem stretching to the line of the desert hills upon which, an enormous triangle, stood the Great Pyramid of Khufu. Two other pyramids, barely visible, but known to be there, were ranged behind it. Standing there twelve miles away, half in shade, half shining in the morning sun, as one struggled into one's vest or fed the silkworms on their breakfast of mulberry leaves, it gave, if anyone in the nursery had thought on those lines, a sense of continuity to human endeavour. Do very small children have thoughts? What remains in the memory is feeling. Passionate surges of delight, anger, grief, affection, terror and surprise imprint on the memory a series of small highly-coloured photographs with blurred edges; brief incidental exposures without before or after. The Great Pyramid was always there, part of the backcloth of the photographs, an impressive solidity that was for ever in the tail of one's eye.

No one told me that the pyramids had been one of the seven wonders of the ancient world, but they were certainly the primal wonder of mine. From early on they exercised an oddly persistent fascination. They could not, it seemed, be taken for granted, like hills and trees and houses. Approached along the pyramid road they got larger and larger and larger until they filled up one half of the sky. It took a long while to ride lurchingly round the Great Pyramid on a camel, and from no angle could their stupendousness be made a thing of nought. They were made of square yellow blocks, exactly like sugar lumps, but higher than I was. Even after the ride, swimming naked in the clear green water of the Mena House swimming bath, they seemed, excitingly, to dominate the scene. And back at home, hours later, there they still were, black against the sunset, which was as usual turning the whole western sky to a bright orange.

'What are they for, Nanny?'

'Tombs, dear. Where's your other sock?'

'Who put them there?'

'The Pharaohs did.'

The Fairoes. Some sort of boy fairies, perhaps? Better not say so and provoke that undignifying adult laughter once again.

'What Fairoes?'

'The Pharaohs, dear. The old kings of Egypt, as you'd know if you'd listened while the master was telling William on the picnic.'

'But what are they *for,* Nanny?' This was a formal question, employed to keep the ball in play. The pyramids had been put there, of course, expressly for my amusement and edification, just as someone had put the stag and the fox and the lamb and the china cottage over the nursery fireplace.

'I've told you before, for the Pharaohs when they died to be buried in.'

'Waiting for the Last Trump?'

'Yes,' Nanny said, knowing better than to hesitate. 'Your other sock is in the doll's bed, and that it got there by itself I beg leave to doubt.'

People were too often, in the kindest manner, scaling one down to size, and laughter was the biggest shot in their locker. The sound of it dented, very slightly, the ruthlessly egocentric world in which, as a two- and three-year-old, one lives. I was, of course, the most important thing that had ever happened. My dignity and independence, my whole separate being and essence, could hardly have mattered more enormously. Other people were shadows, were laps for my sitting on, were arms to pick me up when I was tired, were shoulders for me to rub my bumped head upon. But when they laughed one had a disconcerting impression that people had moments of not sharing this view. I wanted with all my heart to be taken very seriously indeed, and there were times when there seemed to be no takers. Kindly, but in a head-throwing-back fashion, my father laughed and my mother laughed. Nanny and May laughed in a particularly belittling sort of way. Ahmed laughed without restraint, getting every ounce out of it, holding his sides, and Ismaïn laughed derisively, showing the gaps in his teeth, or, more accurately, the rare teeth in his gaps, shaking his head from side to side, as he stopped up a leak in the hose with his extremely dexterous bare feet. Mohammed was a stand-by; dignified, silent and grave. But even his benign chocolate-coloured countenance divided sometimes in amusement around the brilliant whiteness of his teeth.

When I was three my brother William, omniscient already at the age of five, told me that the world was round, and I was impressed with the splendid improbability of this idea. He omitted to mention that we lived on the outside of it, so for many years I dwelt happily in a goldfish bowl with the blue Egyptian sky arched overhead. Others, told the same tale, have thought of it as a huge penny, or the outside of a saucer. The rugged common sense of infancy rejects the notion that we can all be scrambling about on the outside of an orange. To live on the hollow inside of a round world was less improbable and very much cosier. In any case, one was plumb in the middle of the universe, which had no other purpose but to revolve kindly and devotedly around one. Even the ginger biscuits for supper had my initials on them. Wrong way round, but it showed people were trying, had at any rate the right idea.

I learned letters unintentionally, eavesdropping at William's morning lessons, which my mother gave him out of *Reading Without Tears*. Leaning on a small table in the drawing-room, he would contemplate a rather blotchy picture which said that P was a man with a load on his back. Letters felt to be there already somewhere inside one, waiting to be nudged into life, whilst figures obstinately eluded me. I read the letters out loud off a hoarding near the Kasr-el-Nil bridge on a pram walk, R-O-L-L-E-R S-K-A-T-I-N-G R-I-N-K, was aware of a thrill of approbation, of Nanny telling the other nannies that I wasn't two-and-a-half yet. A bright glow settled in my stomach and I repeated the performance; somehow it went down less well a second time. 'That's enough now,' Nanny said, 'or there'll be tears before nightfall.' Importance and grown-upness, briefly held, floated away once again. Babyhood is a happy state from which with tireless energy one battles to be free. It waits all the while to get one back into its sticky clutches. The heaven lying about us in our infancy seems, at the time, more like a treacle well.

Even the things which appear, while one is alone doing them, to be perfectly grown-up, turn out, under adult scrutiny, contrarily. There was that unsettling misunderstanding over the eggs. Coming from a farm near Hanka, four dozen at a time, they sat in a large basket on the hall table. I knew very well what grown-ups did with eggs. They broke them and cooked them and turned them into unpalatable yellow stuff that no sensible person could want to eat. In the vandal world of the kitchen their beautiful roundness and smoothness meant nothing. I took four eggs, and after a happy half hour spent arranging them and rearranging them and rolling them about on cushions, I hid them in a neat row under the sofa in the outer hall for future use. There were hundreds more. Why should anybody miss them?

But they did. Kindly enquiries were made when William and I came down after lunch next day.

'It doesn't matter, darling, but there were four eggs short and we want to know if the farm sent too few. Did you by any chance take some? Tell Mother if you did.'

I could have told her, perhaps, if we had been quite alone. But my father was there, and William; and Ahmed, taking away the pudding plates, and Mohammed, handing round the cheese, and they would quite certainly, some of them, have laughed. I should be revealed before all these as a babyish character who liked playing with eggs, whereas really I was quite different, deeply mature and wise and purposeful. 'No,' I said, hopping from pattern to pattern on the carpet with careless skill. 'No. I didn't.'

The eggs were no longer under the sofa when I looked for them next morning. Perhaps everyone, after all, knew that it was me? No one seemed to be scolded or in trouble, not even the marmitone, the cook's boy, who cried very easily and was not one to hide his grief. He was young and brash and addicted to tearing cheques out of cheque-books and then finding that they were no good without a signature and carefully sticking them back into the cheque-book with stamp paper. Could they have thought it was him, and decided to forgive and forget, because he was the cook's nephew and anyway good at his job? It made for a few days of unease, all the same. If only, if only they wouldn't laugh! Punishment I could have endured. It was grown-up and straightforward and soon over, and carried anyway a certain dignity and importance. It was not diminishing, as laughter was.

Egypt was beautiful and wonderful, the most magical country in the world, if only it hadn't been for India. We spent every summer in England, in a world of cousins, but England was a transit camp, and Egypt was ours. All my Slessor cousins had been in India, at one time or another, because all their fathers were soldiers and it was where soldiers always went.

Egypt was a trump card, incessantly over-trumped by India. India had more of everything, including that very prestigey thing – danger. It was larger, fiercer, and wilder; its people were more numerous and its diseases more lethal. India was a Raj and Egypt a Protectorate. India had the jungle; it had Mowgli, Shere Khan, and Bagheera, characters with whom poor Moses, wailing in his basket amongst the Nile rushes, could hardly be expected to compete.

'The Libyan desert', I informed my cousins, hopefully but inaccurately, 'is full of lions. How many has Uncle Will shot?'

'He shot a man-eating leopard in the Sudan. He shot lots of crocodiles.'

It was no good. Their fathers had all shot tigers, panthers, wild buffaloes, elephants, and in extreme cases, Afghan tribes-men.

'I saw a dead swollen buffalo once, floating in the Nile.' But they had all, it appeared, seen dead swollen *people* floating in the Ganges.

'Where our friends the Dudgeons live, at Hanka, you can hear hyenas laughing in the night.'

'On our way up to Simla,' they countered, 'we camped in the jungle and you could hear the leopards roaring all night long. Quite close. And tiger.'

Their sophistication was electrifying. They even knew to say tiger and not tigers. Would one ever arrive at being so superbly scornful? Thus early do the Joneses raise their never to be drawn level with heads.

I knew about India. I had seen it on the map. It looked like an ice-cream cornet, the froth round the top a spreading range of mountains. Along these, facing north and guarding them, stood Uncle Harold, Uncle Arthur, Uncle Andrew, Uncle Beachy, and Cousin Kerr, backed up by a lot of brave and faithful Indians. Bullets from Afghan and Baluchi tribesmen whistled past their ears and spattered on the mountain rocks. Tribesmen were like tigers, dangerous and shootable but somehow all right, members of the club, players of cricket by different but recognisable rules. But behind the tribesmen was Russia-in-Asia, milling with characters dressed as Yenghiz Khan and emphatically not all right, selling the tribesmen rifles and pushing them on from behind. If any of my uncles relaxed for a moment the Yenghiz Khans would pour down through the mountain passes into the rich plains of India and decimate the inhabitants.

'What's decimate?'

'Cutting people in ten pieces. It's a Roman punishment.'

During brief lulls my uncles took time off to shoot man-eating tigers and give their children rides on their polo ponies or to prevent the brave Indians (Moslems) from chopping up the peaceful Indians (Hindus). It all took a bit of competing with.

'Nothing in India', William said, 'is as old as the pyramids. Or as high.'

This nonplussed the cousins for a moment, for William had a way, even at nine years old, of being right about this sort of thing. 'Oh, *old*,' they said, 'in the Himalayas, which are the highest mountains in the world . . .'

But on the way back from India to England, Egypt unexpectedly showed its teeth at Hamer Stansfeld by giving him sunstroke. 'Not like the sun in *India*,' his nanny had said, allowing him forth in a linen hat. There were doctors and icebags, and a feeling at once of rush and of suspense. 'He's a hundred and five tonight,' the grown-ups said, in hushed voices. It certainly seemed awesomely old. He had been a small boy yesterday, had sunstroke turned him into a tiny little old man? After about a week the Slessor constitution triumphed. Hamer, subdued and slightly thinner, left for Port Said in a sun-helmet.

A mile or so away, across the other branch of the river, dwelt, had I known it, a sympathiser in the Residency in Cairo, Lord Kitchener. He had wanted to be Viceroy of India, and they had fobbed him off and made him High Commissioner of Egypt. He made up for his disappointment by proceeding everywhere in the nearest thing that could be managed to vice-regal state. The splendour of his arrival at church was something to stretch the eyes – the shine and glitter of the horses and harness, their spanking iron-shod pride, arched necks, tossing manes; the swords and the splendours of the escort, the red and gold of the running syces. My heart, underneath a muslin dress with a wide pink sash, expanded with the glory of it. Possibly Kitchener's did too. Upright, stiff, and gleaming, with his running syces clearing the way before him, he was perhaps able to imagine for a moment that he was Rameses or Alexander, although neither of them can have had those very peculiar *mustachios*. Striding up the church path between the canna lilies he seemed stupendous, clinking with medals and giving off a strong dramatic aura of power and vitality. It is improbable that I really remember those eyes close to, focused upon me, that piercing pale blue gaze from irises seemingly too small for their whites. More probably I learnt them later on, from the wartime posters, on which his effigy could be seen, ferociously proclaiming that our King and Country needed us.

Inside, the church, though crammed with people, was cool and quiet, and the roof seemed very high. From outside the roar of Cairo came faintly, the muted ting and rumble of the trams along Boulac, the cries of men with carts. A few flies zizzed in the aisles. The parson, the Reverend C. T. Horan, a retired merchant navy captain, gave off an uncomplicated seafaring holiness, conducting the service in an authoritative but gentle manner. Praying, one could feel the pattern of the hassocks imprinting itself interestingly on one's bare knees. How strange that a few pews in front the proud knees of Kitchener should also be bent to implore the forgiveness of God, which surely could not, in the face of so much glory, be necessary? I implored it with some vigour myself; there had been that business of lying to Nanny over having finished my scrambled eggs at breakfast, when they were, in fact, reposing in the bignonia creeper just below the sewing-room window. Down where I knelt there was a special dusty prayer-bookish smell. For hymns and psalms one stood on the pew, but even then my father seemed very remote and far up.

'Sing the gloria, darling, you know that.' My mother had a

veil tied over her large hat; what would happen if she wanted to blow her nose? Behind the lectern, Kitchener, in implacable tones, was reading the Gospel according to St Mark. Over his shoulder one could just see the figure of Christ in a red cloak in the stained glass east window; they looked unlike, but were they relations? How did people stick in hat-pins without sticking them into their heads?

Sitting on the pew, one could swing one's legs as hard as one liked without their actually hitting the pew behind and causing remonstrance. Wonderful sonorous words emerged from the lined simplicity of Mr Horan's face; his reassuring saintliness came out and embraced one for a fleeting moment of time. The matchless prose of the Book of Common Prayer swam in my ears like some majestic and unearthly sea. There was no question of coming out before the sermon. William and I, aged five and three and unaware of hardship, underwent the full superb stretch.

Church, in time, got rather hot, one's knees stuck together and the piastres for the collection stuck to one's palms. In the churchyard afterwards the sudden brilliance of the sunlight made one blink, made one realize how cool the church had really been. The canna lilies, fire-coloured, were higher than our heads. Our shadows underneath us were gone to nothing in the noonday sun. William wore white shorts and shirt with a dark green tie, white socks and buckled shoes, his black fringe hung down unevenly from under his sun-helmet. My head felt far too hot in a silk-lined straw hat with a wreath of daisies round it.

'Can we go round by Kasr-el-Nil? Can we go round by the lion bridge?'

Foam from the horses' nostrils blew back at us in the river breeze. 'Please, lions, can we come on your bridge? Please lions can we come off your bridge?' Any neglect of this formula would of course have caused the huge bronze lions at either end to descend from their pedestals and devour us. When nothing frightening is happening it is sometimes necessary to invent something frightening that might happen.

At home there was time to visit the rabbits before lunch. William's was black and white, mine all black with a suspicion of one white foot. For coolness' sake their hutch was in one of the arched entrances to the potting shed, facing north, set up upon flower-pots. The rabbits sat far back out of reach, methodically consuming berseem and bran. We lured them forward with milk thistle; still they seemed too far away. There was no time to take them out on to the lawn amongst the beds of snapdragon and ranunculus and phlox drummondii, to lie full length in the February sunshine and worship them in their full rabbitness, to adore their twitching noses and lolloping hind legs and their alert pink-veined ears. Better to get right into the hutch, Sunday clothes and all. Cross-legged, we clasped the rabbits to us; our hearts expanded with rabbit love. How beautiful they were, alive and real and ours. The fur on their bodies quivered, their throbbing hearts beat against us. The milk thistle wept unregarded over William's white shorts. I rocked my rabbit to and fro in a speechless rhythm, my legs pressed into the berseem stalks and the droppings and the spilt water from their drinking bowl. William abruptly moved his foot out of the drinking water, which had begun to soak through his shoes, and the rabbit hutch suddenly jerked off the flower-pots and fell forward on its face.

The world narrowed into a hot confused furry darkness, full of the hind legs of terrified rabbits. Our shouts and screams sounded muffled and ineffective, succeeded only in panicking the rabbits still further. Everything was up-ended and stifling and I was on my head and there was no room to get off it. It seemed a very long time before anybody came.

'My rabbit is dead,' William shouted to our rescuers. 'My rabbit is dead! Its heart has stopped beating! I can't feel its heart!'

'I am dead too,' I pointed out furiously. 'I can't feel my heart either! Nanny! Mohammed! I am dead too,' I wailed persistently. But William, most unfairly, seemed to arouse more sympathy for his grief.

They had found out, too, about the scrambled eggs in the bignonia creeper. The buzzing of many flies had alerted them to its presence.

'Telling a lie', Nanny said, 'and acting a lie.' Everybody looked at me, Nanny and May with grave faces, and Ismaïn, who couldn't understand a word, and Mohammed, who could. The lie was suddenly enormously large, sticking up into the sky, blotting out the sky, bigger than a pyramid, black and dreadful and uncopeable with. I saw that there was green on my pink sash and I knew that I was not a person any more. It was surrender and they knew it and I was a baby again and not even dead and rending the air with an ever louder and wilder boo-hooing.

'There now,' Nanny said. One's grief wrought in her a calm but immediate change of front. Once relegated, one was allowed a new and happy life in Division Four. She picked me up and patted me on my back. 'Come in and get washed for lunch and we'll say no more about it.' Humbled, I held on tightly round her neck, but she was not one for too much of that either. 'There's no call', she pointed out, 'to throttle me.'

England was a far country, it took ten days or a fortnight to get there, and just when one had become used to the ship, it turned into a train. The ocean, a smoking grey chaos, heaved horribly underneath one. Bits of the ship, quite unprovoked, came arbitrarily at one and hit one in the forehead. Even Nanny, indignantly appealed to, seemed unable to make it stop rocking. A swing was one thing, and very enjoyable; but this thing went up and down and up and down, and one could not, apparently, get off when the pastime became boring. It had its pleasurable side; the cabin trunks slid out from under the bunks and the nauseous condensed milk shot over the top of one's mug without any human aid and spilled all over the floor of the dining saloon. Calmer weather too brought its enjoyments. The other passengers stuffed one with chocolates at illicit hours, making it impossible to eat boiled fish when the time for boiled fish came. I discovered the enchanting sport of sitting on the deck with my feet through the railings and then drawing them sharply back so that my shoes fell into the sea. It was wonderful how often one could do this without being caught in the act; I once arrived at Tilbury with no shoes at all. There was the spinning drop, the moment of floating, the suck and swirl as one's footwear disappeared for ever into the foam, whence not all the nannies in the world could retrieve it. Fun could also be had in this respect with the P. and O. Steamship Company's teaspoons.

My most loved object at this time was a bright blue collar box containing four red Christmas tree candles and a doll's arm. Never for any *thing* have I felt such a love, such a burning passion of possession as I felt for this. The obsession of very small children with valueless objects is such that one wonders why anyone bothers to buy them toys, able as they are to draw total happiness from a collection of used bus-tickets. The box was square, blue, and bright, the candles were twisted and yet straight, in a delectable manner, and the doll's arm was curving, human, and pale pink. On journeys to and from England it was impossible, even in sleep, to detach myself from it. Harsh voices shouted before and behind as I stumped along French railway platforms, clutching the blue collar box to that stout indeterminate stomach that one has at two and three years old and again in the fifties and sixties, as if there alone lay comfort and assurance. Once, shatteringly, it fell from me under a stationary French train; I lay with it in spirit on the flints until a kind French porter in a blue blouse retrieved it, complete with every last candle. Different fields, trees, houses, rivers, flashed past; different faces smiled, frowned, looked blankly; the collar box stayed with me, absolutely square, ravishingly blue, and always the same.

England, once arrived at, consisted mainly of Hampshire, interspersed with little bits of Devonshire. It was a place of seemingly endless green lawns, inhabited by seemingly endless relations. Far too many of these were called Cousin Nell, or Cousin Daisy, and took what seemed a disproportionate interest in one. We had, after all, only that moment met. On some stone steps was my Slessor grandfather, a white beard, a feeling of strength and kindness, of sternness and of soap. He had many grandchildren older and doughtier than I was; I came towards the tail end of a long procession. He was one of those rare and excellent grown-ups who did not start kissing one until they knew one well. He remained upright and made no demands, and yet seemed prepared to listen to my traveller's tales. He had been born in 1821, six years after the Battle of Waterloo, and had lived right through Victoria's reign and out the other end. He was about to survive Edward the Seventh, and would probably be with us yet, had he not, at the age of ninety-one, fallen off a ladder while pruning a climbing rose and broken his leg. We were separated by eighty-seven years. After a short conversation he held out his hand to me, and I felt able to relax my grasp upon the blue collar box. I accepted a banana from him on my way to bed, and this interview was all that ever passed between us, but it was enough to make me sure that I liked him.

'Would you like to have this little pink glass, dear?' The water in it was pink too; spilt all over the tablecloth for purposes of verification it revealed itself as the usual disappointing no-colour. There were little cries, and a bustle; in some ways it was a not unsatisfactory experiment. In the garden the gunnera leaves were large green umbrellas under which one could comfortably stand. This was Devonshire and I was two. The ladies, still uttering little cries, passed over the lawn carrying frilly parasols, their dresses trailed after them. Their hats were like dishes piled high with fruit and flowers and with the wings of birds as in a still-life picture, visible only in tantalizing flashes as they bent down to kiss one. Utterers of high clear laughter, they followed each other across the lawns, declaring that things were deliciously pretty. Faintly incalculable, they seemed agreeable enough and probably were: wives, mothers, aunts, in the main loving and faithful, out of habit, inclination, upbringing, effort, or the absence of any alternative course. Tying on motoring veils over their enormous hats, they climbed into very high motor-cars, whose brass carriage lamps were lit by oil and could be detached for the better observation of signposts. Sometimes, for a treat, I climbed in after them, wearing an identical motoring veil and a coat with many capes like a highwayman's; a circular indignant face surrounded by an excessive quantity of curly fair hair. William climbed in too, in boots with stripey linings, a coat with a very wide collar, and an enormous flat cap. We proceeded along the crown of the road at about thirty miles an hour through a countryside permanently bathed in sunshine and in dust. Over their sweeping dresses the mothers and aunts wore long tussore dust coats, which were very necessary. The countryside of Edwardian England was beautiful, unravished, and, by some freak of the memory, extremely dry. Dust powdered the lower leaves of spreading beech trees, rose up in clouds behind our wheels, lay white along hedges cut and laid with the unhurried precision of craftsmen. The bracken fronds, the bluebells and the pink campions along the Devon banks were all snowed over with a rosy powder. Through this untroubled landscape the high-seated cars chugged uncertainly; the women, who never drove (and never smoked) peering out with innocently wayward eyes through thick layers of silk gauze.

'Don't suck your veil, darling; look what a horrid patch it's made.'

The whole thing was very exciting and glamorous and one left home with a sense of adventure and arrived back with a sense of achievement, and shot round the house telling everyone that one had been out in the motor. A drive was a sufficient object in itself, one did not drive just to get somewhere, and people were known to have to go and lie down afterwards to recover from the excitement and fatigue.

Not all Edwardian men can have had such very long legs: possibly it was one's viewpoint that gave one this impression. Their far up faces, above unaccountably deep collars, seemed always to be breaking into laughter. Their salient characteristic was their relaxedness, a kind of easy-going panache glossing their words and actions. Their legs in narrow trousers carrying them inexhaustibly up hill, or thrown, in gleaming leggings, over a horse's back, moved with an unhurried and purposeful élan. Their voices, heard in mockery, affection, or sternness, rang always with that confident buoyancy that was to sink for ever in the mud of the Great War battlefields, with that unquestioning sense of the rightness and fitness of the Pax Britannica and of their place within it. They basked in what they imagined to be its high noon, in what were in fact its last rays, in the sun never setting upon the regimental band playing selections from H.M.S. *Pinafore* under the banyan tree. Consciously Christians, of a sort, they fought the good fight against an excess in drinking, smoking, or spending; against paying insufficient regard to mothers-in law or dull old relations. They believed in practically everything except Father Christmas and votes for women, and it made for great peace of mind. Straddling the world, with their graceful wives and their strangely over-dressed babies, they believed in marital fidelity and in kindness to animals which included their rapid despatch when they were being shot, hunted, or fished for. They believed in right and wrong, with a strong line drawn between. They were listening without self-consciousness to the last faint echoes of Roland's horn. They said family prayers, and made endless practical jokes, and tipped one golden half sovereigns. To later critics they could be said to have lived in an innocent, callous, enjoying dream, in some ways perhaps never quite growing up. But they were true to their ethic, and remained, even to people who were not their relations, curiously lovable. Their self-mastery, and not only or mainly in sexual matters, was truly adult; and when the appalling calamity of World War I avalanched over them, they confronted it without self-pity. From their loss we all still suffer. In their rare and more perspicacious survivor, Churchill, we all rejoice. There was something marvellously entire about them.

The love-hate relationship between the English and the animal world was never more passionately displayed than in Edwardian houses. One could hardly cross a drawing-room floor without falling over the snarling head of a lion's skin, or a polar bearskin stretched out upon it. The hideous archaic profiles of rhinoceroses leant out of walls, over the Zanzibar chests in the outer halls. Hollowed-out feet of elephants containing potted palms were dotted about halls where the garishness of Turkey carpets alternated with the smoother surfaces of Persian rugs. Inkstands were made from the hooves of favourite hunters or chargers, doors were kept open by the stuffed feet of eland. Behind the shut doors of smoking-rooms, whence the smell of cigar smoke drifted richly out, would be stags' heads, wild buffalo horns jutting out of hollow skulls, the heads of black panthers with gleaming yellow glass eyes. Tiger skins hung on landings; their huge teeth menaced one on one's way to bed. No billiard room was innocent of stuffed white owls, stuffed badgers, plaster salmon; even sometimes a stuffed albatross, enormous and yellowing, regarded one malignly out of its beady eye. Horrendous re-created pike lurked in the pantry passages; in the dusk they seemed as big as sharks. In the hall of my godmother's house near Barnstaple there was a stuffed bear, upright, holding in his paws a brass tray for the reception of visiting cards. By daytime he was friendly, almost cosy, could be nearly thought of as a pet. At twilight he became menacing, in the dark he threatened terrifyingly. To cross a hall on one's way to bed was to encounter, close to, all the perils of a jungle at night.

There must have been, in fact there certainly was, pretty furniture, as well as china and pictures; but all, to the infant eye, obscured behind a feral haze. Through these natural-history museum houses grown-ups swept or strode unaccountably in and out of one's life; exciting, alarming, impermanent; exuding interesting smells of scent or of cigars, and never quite believed in. Reality dwelt at this time in the starched lap of Nanny, despite her confusing tendency to equate moral virtue with the regular movement of the bowels. 'Be good now, Priscilla dear,' they said, all the time, in connection with absolutely everything. But what was goodness, anyway? It was something which, like the Joneses, was never to be quite caught up with. And even when one had, or so it seemed, briefly caught up with it and was out of trouble for a day or two, one was whirled inexplicably away to another country there to start the whole defeating process again with what appeared to be a different set of rules. In Egypt no one minded one's sitting on the grass, in England they came at one with cries of remonstrance for doing just this. In England no one said anything if one went out without a hat; to do the same thing in Egypt was to invite them to come running after one in a rare taking. To wander through the English fields was all right, to wander through the fields of Zamalek was unthinkable, was forbidden with a sternness that even I could recognize. To comply with all injunctions was not humanly possible; really it was simpler to let the whole thing ride and enjoy life. Except that, hamperingly, one loved them, and they minded. One had moments of painful affection, of a lavish desire to do what they wanted. But these passed in a flash, leaving long days and weeks of blissful oblivion when one lived solidly in the world of immediate preoccupation, a world holding only the mud-pie of the moment.

Lying in bed on those long summer evenings, looking at the square of bright blue sky beyond the window, one sometimes felt locked in eternity, as if the light could never dim, and sleep could never come. Thoughts splashed in one's brain; the water-fall words of the day flowed over one. The mystery of what sinks in in infancy and what flows by is profound; a child a baffling mixture of receptivity and inattention. Waves of words, breaking continually over the impressionable sand, leave weed and stick and broken glass and echoing shell, and sweep as much away. Another tide takes some, brings more; how much unaccountably sinks down to become part of the permanent structure of the shore? Nanny words, reading aloud words, caressing mother words, half-heard snatches of conversation, of poetry, praise, blame, exhortation; why does some float by and why does some sink in? *Wipe your mouth, say your grace, tell the truth, keep your elbows off the table.* There are words so immediate and poignant that they could have been said yesterday, and are said for ever. *Sir, come down e'er my child die.* One swings abruptly from world to world. *Don't care was made to care, Don't care was hanged. Take off your hat, William, to Mr and Mrs Dallin. Spare your breath to cool your porridge. And he would fain have filled his belly with the husks that the swine did*

*eat. This little pig went to market, this little pig stayed at home.
Blow bugles, blow, set the wild echoes flying, And answer, echoes,
answer, dying, dying, dying. Say please, say yes, say thank you, say
sorry, say how do you do? For thine is the kingdom, the power, and
the glory. Once upon a time there were four little rabbits whose
names were Flopsy, Mopsy, Cottontail, and Peter. Fold your vest,
and clean your teeth, and say your prayers. Nobly, nobly, Cape St
Vincent to the North West died away; Sunset ran, one glorious
blood-red, reeking into Cadiz Bay; Love me, kiss me, Hug me
tight. Never kiss a lady with your hat on, William! It's no use
grumbling, it's no use fussing, it's no use crying over spilt milk.*

A mingling of folk-lore, impatience, platitude, affection; a
jumble of eternal verity and country precept and temporary
slang pours out daily over minds half-hearing, half-differen-
tiating, alternately open as a sieve or retentive as clay. Subtly,
day by day, words mould our prejudice, our apprehensions,
joys, desires, the unconscious ethic by which we live.

*Humpty-Dumpty sat on the wall, Humpty-Dumpty had a
great fall. That's no way to hold your spoon. Oxus forgetting the
bright speed he had In his high mountain cradle of Pamere. For
what we have received the Lord make us truly thankful. Say, no
thank you, say, Yes please. Don't cough over the table. Say, I beg
your pardon.* Reiterated words, falling with the persistence of
steadily dropping water and channelling their permanent
grooves in the sand: shadowy words, scarce heard and less
understood, dappling the landscape of the mind with the
mysterious charm and rhythm of their sounds. *It was no season then for her To wanton with the sun her lusty paramour.*

Finish your mouthful before you speak. Mind the step, and shame the devil, and shut the door behind you. Never ask a man his income, never ask a woman her age. I saw three ships come sailing by, sailing by, sailing by, I saw eternity the other night Like a great ring of pure and endless light.

A beguilement of words, a tumbling cataract of sounds, and how much of all is absorbed, and why, penetrating the steady self-enchanted dream of life?

II

In the middle of the eighteen eighties, John Henry Slessor, rector of Headbourneworthy in Hampshire, decided abruptly that he must marry again, and this decision very nearly caused us not to be. He came to dislike his second wife so much that he declined ever to be left alone with her. My mother, Alethea, was the most dutiful of his four pretty daughters, and as the other three were all in India and his two sons were serving abroad, she remained at home in the role of a buffer state until she was well into her late thirties. From this Andromeda-like situation she was rescued by my father, a purposeful and cheerful Perseus called William Hayter.

Upon reaching his decision to re-marry, John Henry wasted no time. He proceeded to Wiesbaden where the lady of his choice, a Mrs Scudamore, was taking the waters. It had never occurred to him that he might be refused; nor was he. Returning to Headbourneworthy he led his four daughters into the rose garden, where he communicated the news to them. All four of them ungratefully burst into tears; not the last to be shed about their step-mother. 'If she had been a bit less pious and a bit more human,' my father later commented, 'she might have had a better time.' What dictated my grandfather's choice in this matter has never been made clear, except that he wanted

a chaperone for his just growing-up daughters and Mrs Scudamore was quite awesomely respectable. Can she have been
attractive? Judging by photographs – no. Her first husband had
been a good general, a good shot, and a good judge of a horse;
perhaps it was felt that this made him also a good judge of a
woman. Herbert and Arthur Slessor, her two step-sons, came
to dislike Mrs Scudamore so much that they preferred to forget
her memory and never wrote her name in the family tree, so it
is impossible to tell when she married or died. None of her
step-children would ever talk of her. *De mortuis nil nisi bonum*;
therefore in this case *de mortuis nil.*

John Henry had sound reasons for wanting a chaperone for
his daughters. Charlotte Fennessy, his first wife and the
mother of his six children, an oval-faced black-haired
Irishwoman, who had died four years previously, had been all
that was good and sweet, but there could have been some
doubt in his mind about how his daughters might turn out.
His own antecedents were of course impeccable; it is only
from the stock of our in-laws that we look for trouble.
Charlotte Slessor's father, Robert Fennessy, had been illegiti-
mate; son of Charles Stewart (3rd Marquess of Londonderry
and younger brother of the statesman), by the daughter of his
Irish coachman; she was said to be very beautiful except for
her fat legs. Whenever fat legs recurred in the Slessor family
they were put down, most unfairly and with none but hearsay
evidence, to the coachman's daughter. Nor was this all. Robert
Fennessy, brought up and educated by his father and given a
job as a king's messenger and a house in Wilton Place, had

married a Miss Wilson, child of one of the daughters of Admiral Lord Rodney by a runaway match with a wild young man called Wilson. Who was Wilson? Why did they have to run away? Perhaps he had some lethal disability such as possessing no land. Where did they run to? Could he have been, unthinkably, *a married man*? Vague isolated facts filter down through a haze of Victorian reticence. We were only told about Lord Londonderry and the coachman's daughter when we were quite grown up and then only *à propos* of someone's legs not being quite up to scratch. But the whole business made John Henry thoughtful. Suppose, like poor Henrietta Rodney, his daughters should grow up to throw their caps over the windmill? To allow a daughter to stray might be forgivable in Admiral Rodney, permanently occupied as he was in sinking the French. For discouraging any frivolous eighteenth-century trend towards illegitimacy in his descendants, Mrs Scudamore must have seemed to John Henry just the ticket.

The Slessor antecedents were solid in the extreme. Rendered practically immortal by many generations spent battling with the climate of Aberdeenshire, they descended on the soft south via the British army in the late seventeenth century. John Henry's constitution had been further fortified by the lives of his immediate forbears, which had consisted of hard soldiering, good food, cold baths, faith in God, and a general absence of nervous stress. The usual high proportion of sons were carried off by cannon balls or lost at sea, although John Henry's father and grandfather lived long enough to become generals. But of his two uncles, William Edward died as a soldier, aged sixteen, and Henry Thomas, lieutenant R.N., was killed in action aged twenty-four, fighting under Admiral Sir Sydney Smith in the Napoleonic wars, and described by his commanding officer as 'brave, affectionate and mild, a rising ornament to his profession'. Only one of John Henry's four brothers lived into middle age. The number of families in England that have been kept in existence entirely by the non-celibacy of the clergy must be legion. Celibacy, a finicking continental notion brought in by William the Conqueror, who found half the priests in England married (and doubtless surrounded by large flaxen-haired broods, constantly spilling the mead and generally getting underfoot but ultimately worth it), so wrought upon Norman and Plantagenet life that practically no families survived into Tudor times, but when under Elizabeth I the ban was reluctantly relaxed, survival set in. Six out of seven family sons might be, often were, killed in foreign or in civil wars, or by disease. Dynastically, no matter. Far away in some Norfolk, Gloucestershire, or Yorkshire rectory, Edmund, the eighth son, supplied with a modest income and supplying himself with a pretty wife, was unconcernedly chugging out a fresh set of Rogers, Henrys, Williams, Thomases, Charleses, Johns and Stephens, to be mown down, swept overboard, burnt up by Flemish or Indian fevers, and generally far-flung; the most intelligent or biddable among them being usually reserved for the family living, there to repeat the whole process over again. What it did for religion could be questioned; what it did for our national life was greatly to enrich it by the provision of such diverse characters as Ben Jonson, Hobbes, Jane Austen, Lord Nelson, Coleridge, Sir Joshua Reynolds, John Wesley, James Wolfe, and all those very singular Brontës.

The only untoward event in my grandfather's family had taken place on the other side of the Atlantic (which somehow made it better), when his grandmother's first cousin, Major André, had been executed as a spy. Dispatched by General Clinton on a cross-country journey through enemy territory to treat with Benedict Arnold, he had exchanged his red coat for a brown one. On his way back he was captured by American troops. In spite of a dignified letter to George Washington requesting to be shot as a soldier rather than hanged as a felon, the Americans, unable to catch Benedict Arnold and needing to take his treachery out on someone, strung him up. But he was so handsome, and his bearing so brave, that no one in this small community could at first be found to do the deed. At last an obliging fellow, blacking his face to preserve anonymity, carried out the sentence. To the lasting credit of this not very rich community, the valuable diamond solitaire signet ring mounted in heavy gold which John André wore was taken from his dead finger and returned to his sisters in England, and his body was later dug up and buried in Westminster Abbey; but no one likes to think of their near relations treading air, in boots and breeches however well cut and to this rule John Henry Slessor was no exception. This execution was, however, generally thought by the Slessors and indeed by some Americans to be far from cricket. From his grandmother, Harriet Bristow, John Henry inherited private means, a large quantity of tobacco leaf china which came from her French forbears, the Girardots, and the diamond ring and collection of leather-bound poems which had belonged to Major André. To this collection of china and furniture, my grandfather slowly added; his tastes were mercifully Georgian, and even the restorations which he carried out upon his Saxon church could have been, for one of his Victorian generation, very much worse. In between his duties he worked off his immense energy in long cross-country walks or rides, in gardening, in making inlaid tables, and in translating the whole of Virgil's *Aeneid* in rhyming couplets.

Looked back upon from a more humane and less rigorous age, the well-to-do Victorians leave an impression of a strange acquiescence in the miseries about them. John Henry took in the works of Charles Dickens in monthly parts, as they came out, and delighted in them; he cannot therefore have been ignorant of the appalling conditions in which most of his countrymen lived. Although country people were never so neglected, underfed, or ill-treated as in the towns, there must have been plenty of misery and poverty around him. There was in fact a widow at Abbotsworthy who brought up a family of nine children entirely upon vegetables and snail soup. That he denied himself to help poor people was as true of him as of many another sincere country parson. But rich and poor had existed throughout recorded time; and to believe that things which seemed as much a part of the natural order as night and day could ever be radically altered, required a leap of the imagination for which very few people who were not themselves poor had the necessary spiritual agility. He did what he could for his immediate neighbours and prayed for the rest; living, as most people do, within the ethic of his day, which was sterner and more self-disciplined than ours but less awakened and less imaginative.

The eldest son, Bert, was serving in the Mediterranean when his father married again. Tall, long-headed, and handsome, with a crisp voice and observant blue eyes, he was a Slessor in the brave, affectionate, and mild tradition, and inspired great confidence; if he had been at home his father might possibly have listened to words of caution. Arthur, the next eldest, was grey-eyed and rather more dashing; a magnificently well-made man, with a long-jawed throwaway charm; though certainly brave he was not conspicuously affectionate and only intermittently mild. He had just come back with his regiment from the West Indies, where, beset by yellow fever, they had died in great numbers. He himself was so desperately ill that his companions, not knowing about the Slessor constitution, had made his coffin and engraved his name on it and marched some miles in the hot sun to dig his grave. He brought the coffin home to substantiate this tale, and because it is one of those few things that cannot fail to come in useful. In fact he had no need of it for another sixty years. It hung about in the stables, getting underfoot, until someone hit on the notion of making it into a toboggan. Both sons received the news of their impending step-mother with misgiving.

This marriage of convenience might have worked if both

sides had been honest, or even reasonable, instead of only one. But Mrs Scudamore demanded as by right an instant affection and acceptance that she was unlikely to get from a closely-knit family of six children who had very much loved their own mother. Failing to receive more than duty or manners demanded, she went off into a kind of martyred twenty-five-year sulk.

In one way she fulfilled her function. All her step-children were safely married; two of them, of course outliving their spouses, married twice. But whatever the Slessors felt about their step-mother, they were not of a fibre to be precipitated into marriage a minute before they wanted to be. Life at Headbourneworthy continued upon its even way, and no one married for the next ten years. Arthur was the first, marrying a very tall and beautiful Miss Cotesworth who was typically called Tiny. They had three sons and a daughter. The eldest of these, an enchanting, fiendish little boy with curly hair and round blue eyes, a nanny's terror, developed a bad cold when he was three years old. 'I can't do nothing with him,' his nanny complained a few days later, appealing for parental support, 'he's naughtier than ever. Every time I stand him up to dress him, he just falls down!' Johnny, who later became Jack, had in fact had polio, which in the nineties was virtually never diagnosed, and limped from then onwards, all the way through to the top of the R.A.F.

Soon after this the girls' orchestra was broken up. Bay, the pianist, the youngest and the most attractive, was the first to go, falling in love with a dashing Irishman called Beauchamp

Magrath, a soldier, home on leave from India. John Henry had always been friends with Beachy's parents, and was therefore inclined to look favourably upon Beachy. His father was a general, and John Henry, himself the son and grandson of generals, seems to have had a deeply built-in conviction that the sons of generals were faithworthy. Certainly they were madly in love, had enough to live upon, and reasonable prospects. He and Bay departed for India where they danced all night and won gymkhanas all day and were extremely happy. On his next leave Beachy brought a friend to Headbourneworthy, Harold Stansfeld, also the son of a general, also in an Indian regiment; one of those tall rather silent long-jawed Yorkshiremen who produce an effect of inexhaustible reliability which in his case was justified by the facts. Calm and handsome, he was a passionate naturalist, and would, if pressed, recount tiger-shooting tales of a bloodcurdling kind in a slow unexcited voice. It was clear that during the course of a hunt for a man-eating tiger, he became, like Jim Corbett in later years, devoted to it, and deeply admiring of its strategy and tactics. A note of melancholy and regret would creep into his voice as he neared the moment of the tiger's demise; you could tell he was longing for it to make yet another brilliant getaway. There were, after all, a great many Indians, and not all that many tigers. He married the third sister, Agnes, the 'cellist of the family, small, quiet and bookish, with a curly fringe and large appealing blue eyes; the least pretty but probably the most intelligent.

The next to get married was Bertie. Thought by his family

to be lazy about women (who were only too disinclined to be lazy about him), he followed the line of least resistance and married a younger Miss Cotesworth. Both sisters had been warmly in favour of this double relationship, but once they had achieved it, they never got on so well again, thus perceptibly disorientating for a short while what had always previously been an unruffled brotherhood.

The eldest of the four sisters was called Meg as in *Little Women*, and like her, she was very pretty, full of the sort of silliness that can be charming in a young woman and infinitely irritating later on, fond of making jams and jellies, and with a species of Victorian elder sister bossiness which to her younger sisters seemed quite natural and right. She had a perfect complexion, and an eighteen-inch waist of which she was extremely vain, a beautiful profile and large blue eyes, and a lovely slim upright figure which she retained into her late seventies. She played the violin, and frequently wore clusters of roses pinned here and there about her dresses, and uttered little shrieks of dismay, and was in short exactly the kind of character destined to refuse many better men and set up latish in life with a small, handsome, and amazingly obstinate Bengal Lancer. Andrew Barnard, descendant of a similarly named Peninsular War hero, was an excellent polo player and a fair shot; on a horse, and as a Bengal Lancer, with turban, long-sashed tunic, and lance, he looked superb. Once off his horse and out of his uniform, he dwindled sadly, was revealed as being rather short, and seemed never again to have a thing to do.

Out of all this family there now remained only my mother, the second daughter, Alethea. She had been a shy, dark-haired little girl, adoring her mother, and shattered by her death. The cancer which had killed Charlotte Slessor had not been diagnosed until too late. John Henry had that inability which often goes with extremely good health, of realizing illness in another without the help of obvious symptom or reiterated complaint. But Alethea, then thirteen years old, did realize, with an agonised apprehension, what was about to happen. Her mother's death left her with a kind of deep basic sadness which lingered somewhere in her being for the rest of her life. It left her with a blank which nothing could fill, least of all a sulking malingering step-mother who had married her father because he was a handsome widower with a comfortable home. Nor, kind and affectionate though he always was, could she ever really talk freely with her father. The convention of the day made it almost impossible, and in any case John Henry was one of those many Englishmen, prevalent down the ages and still with us in some force, who are so attractive to women that they never have to bother to find out what they are really like.

To leave home was of course unthinkable, both duty and affection enjoined her to stay where she was so much wanted. Victorian girls had never heard of frustration, and the deeply believed in rightness of what they were doing gave their lives a kind of restfulness and fulfilment. Victorian fathers, with their exacting and authoritarian ways, often and justifiably inspired horror and hatred in their children. They also, less notoriously, inspired a great deal of admiration and a great deal of love. They lived hard themselves, thought deeply about their decisions and stuck to them when once they were made, and could not be wheedled, cajoled, or pressurized out of them. Everyone connected with them knew exactly where they stood, and this gave a certain solidity and calm to family life. It was a system which causes disgust and rebellion in the hearts of their descendants, but it made, strangely enough, for much domestic happiness. All, of course, depended upon the character of the father.

Earlier on, before anyone married, there had been cheerful times. There were the tableaux, dressing up and holding the pose while the draught whistled through the village hall or the long drawing-room. The Seasons had been the most effective one of all, Bay with her auburn hair as autumn, Meg as spring, Agnes as summer with sheaves of corn, Al as winter, in white velvet with cotton wool snowflakes in her hair. There had been the tennis, the picnics, the indefatigable bicycling expeditions, and, when the brothers were at home, jaunts to Portsmouth or to the races. There had been the staying away, the quartet playing in other people's village halls and drawing-rooms – 'But how did you travel all over the country with a harp and everything?'

'Perfectly straightforward, my harp and Ag's cello went in the guard's van and came up in the wagonette. And after we'd played some classical music we all took out our banjoes and played and sang popular songs. It was *delightful* and we loved it. And so, I think, did everyone else.'

There had also been the balls, the parties, the private dances, strawberries and cream at Bramstons on the days of the Eton Match, the long drives about the Hampshire countryside, then virtually unchanged since Jane Austen's day. There was that eerie clump of trees on the Newbury road where the horses always shied because a highwayman had once hung there in chains. As to dances, 'There was never any question of our taking partners with us, our brothers were generally abroad and we arrived in a bunch, four girls, and had always a wonderful time. What's the fun of going to dances when you *know* who your partners will be? We would have thought that very tame.'

They stayed about, in Devonshire, in Hertfordshire with the Wigrams, in Scotland where a first cousin, Hyacinth Scott-Kerr, a beautiful and wayward woman, had married a dull Lord Howard of Glossop; a glimpse of a formal, secretive, on-the-defensive Catholic family life, with oysters and wild duck for the Friday fast. The fact that he was a Roman Catholic far outweighed the goodness of his family; it was thought of as a sad mésalliance, and she was known in the family, quite without malice, as 'poor dear Hy'. They reacted with the kind of rather self-conscious niceness that would now be employed by a similar family upon the marriage of a cousin to a highly respected Ghanaian. Then there were friends near Salisbury, and moonlit riding picnics to Stonehenge, then unfenced in and little visited. Life was so sheltered, and so safe and static, that they turned with delight away from it into the challenge and danger of India.

Hampshire seemed very flat to Alethea when the others had all gone. But she enjoyed a great many things and was never one for self-pity. There was plenty to do in the parish, there was gardening, which she had always loved, there was playing with little nephews and nieces, pale from India or rosy from the seaside at Sidmouth. She escaped for an occasional visit, went to sales, collected in a modest way china, Bristol glass, Georgian mahogany furniture. Like many another lonely English countrywoman she took increasingly to horses, driving a tandem in and around the country lanes and to shop in Winchester. 'You surely didn't drive a thing like that with two horses one in front of the other right into *Winchester*?' 'Of course.' 'How did you manage in those narrow streets?' 'It was sometimes a bit awkward where the narrow end of Jewry Street comes into the High Street, the leading horse was always well round the corner before one could hope to see anything.' Her cousin, Bob Scott-Kerr, a young man in the Grenadiers, had a four-in-hand in which he drove her down from London to Ascot for the races; on other less conspicuous occasions she was allowed to take the reins herself. But there must have been moments when she allowed herself a faint sigh for life floating slowly by in the late Victorian twilight.

Of the three or four men who during this time wanted to marry her she was certainly in love with one. He was a romance of the hunting field, but it was no good, he lived in the north, and she saw no possibility of ever being able to leave home. They would ride home together after hunting, she on her mare Jeanette, wearing one of those sweeping and unfairly romantic side-saddle habits. With what sad words of love did she refuse him, coming back along the Hampshire downs, scuffling through the beechwoods in the mild soundless dusks of early winter? She came home alone. It was lambing time, the shepherd was lighting his lamp in the stable yard. An old man, he wore a smock and used always to lead his sheep, he thought scorn of any shepherd that had to drive his sheep along. Inside the rectory that had once been so noisy and cheerful it was now very quiet. There would be dinner with Father, off Worcester plates, family news, parish talk, claret out of gold-patterned Bristol glass, unspoken relief that the step-mother was having dinner upstairs in her room.

A few years later my father appeared on the scene. From the first he was perfectly decided. She must and should marry him. There was a daughter-in-law soon to be settled at Halterworth near Romsey who could take her turn in looking after the old man. Her sisters' children were getting too old for India, they would soon be home with their mothers for long stretches of time. With a sigh of relief my mother felt able to believe him. They were married at Headbourneworthy in August 1905 and lived happily ever afterwards.

There is a photograph of my parents in the summer of their courtship on the Lawn at Goodwood. My mother's long white dress has a ruffle round the hem, its fullness trails out over the lawn behind her. She has the same ruffle round her hat. My father is wearing a straw hat, but Uncle Bert, also there with his wife, is rather more up-to-date and is extremely smart in a Homburg. It was in 1904, and they all look lapped in

Edwardian peace, but perhaps they had simply backed a winner.

William Hayter was no stranger. His parents were family friends. As a boy at Winchester he had spent leave-out days at Headbourneworthy Rectory and been indiscriminately in love with all four sisters, but more particularly with Aunt Bay, always relaxed and responsive, and his exact contemporary in age. After Oxford he became a barrister and spent his long vacations in sailing or in travelling round Europe; his paths did not cross Slessor paths. At some moment towards the end of the century life in London as a young barrister suddenly seemed to him unbearably stuffy and he went to the Sudan. Perhaps he too had a frustrating love affair.

Africa at this time exerted the sort of pull upon young men that outer space now exerts, and seemed not much less dangerous or remote. His job was in the recently pacified western Sudan, and he spent some years there as a judge on circuit. From there he went into the Egyptian administration, in order to be able to marry my mother; English women not being at that time allowed into the Sudan. He left the rigours and simplicities of life in the Sudan with regret, to involve himself in the tortuous labyrinths and the complicated tensions of multi-racial Cairo. Whether his happy marriage made the exchange worthwhile or whether the fascinating complexities of Egyptian life got him gradually in their grip I do not know; he seemed to me an abundantly happy man. And life in Cairo, whatever else, is never dull.

Shortly after my father's arrival in Egypt he was summoned in the ordinary course to a reception at the Abdin Palace. The Khedive Abbas Hilmy, conversing briefly with each group of guests as was his wont, approached my father with some interest, as he had so recently come from the depths of the Sudan, a country over which the Egyptians claimed suzerainty and which they regarded with a mixture of horror and fascination and visited as seldom as possible.

'And how', the Khedive demanded, at the end of his questionnaire, 'did you manage for women in Kordofan?'

My father replied that he was engaged to be married to a girl in England.

'Ah yes, England,' the Khedive conceded, brushing aside this irrelevancy. His mind did not encompass the reality of such a place, and dwelt happily in a rhomboid formed by Paris, Istanbul, Baghdad and Cairo. 'But I wish to know how you liked the women in the Sudan. How about the little negresses, how are they?'

My father replied that he had had no carnal knowledge of the little negresses.

The Khedive regarded him with bland Turkish incredulity.

'You were three years in the Sudan, without the least little negress?'

'I had leave, Excellency, during those three years.'

'But in the Sudan you existed without one, without any little negress?'

'Yes.'

'Without the smallest, the most minuscule, little negress?'

'Without', my father replied firmly, 'the least little negress.'

This circumstance caught the fancy of the Khedive. Continuing his circulation of the room, he approached each successive group exclaiming, in his heavy Turkish French – *'Vous voyez, messieurs, ce grand gaillard là-bas, ce jeune homme Hayter? Il a passé trois ans au Sudan sans une seule petite négresse, sans, il m'assure, la moindre petite négresse.'* It was some months before the delighted laughter of Cairo died down.

My father was the seventh in a family of sixteen, thirteen of whom grew up, and like the seventh wave, he was the biggest and the best. The history of the Hayter family is boringly usual. They sound Saxon, and first appear after the Wars of the Roses as yeoman farmers in the Wylye valley in Wiltshire. Over the generations they enriched themselves, married well, started being educated in the seventeenth century, and built Roche Court at Winterslow near Salisbury, a manor that by the eighteenth century they had come to own, and a neat little row of almshouses in Fisherton Street, Salisbury. By the marriage of John Hayter to Grace Goodenough in 1770 they also acquired the manor of Winterbourne Stoke near Amesbury. By the early nineteenth century they threw up Sir George Hayter, the painter, son of the landscape gardener who helped Beckford at Fonthill, and Sir William Hayter, a successful lawyer and politician who became Lord Haversham. They seemed however to be non-holders-on; clever enough to get there, not dogged enough to stay there; Whigs, but with a Tory habit of drinking too much and getting themselves killed hunting. One of them approached a five-barred gate at full gallop in a dog-cart under the impression that he was riding and not driving, with results that proved fatal. Lord Haversham carelessly allowed himself to die out. Francis Hayter, the liveliest son, a retired admiral, went away to settle in New Zealand. The houses and land were sold. Haversham's youngest nephew, Henry Hayter, my grandfather, was sent up to London in the 1850s to make his fortune. This he succeeded in doing. But he light-headedly invested the whole of it and his wife's not inconsiderable fortune as well, in China, and his youngest child had hardly been christened before he lost the lot, and was left with nothing much beside the very large London house he had bought to house them all.

He had married Janet Druce, rather small and square, with blue eyes, a beaky dominating nose ('Of course the Druces were Norman, de Ros,' one of the aunts said, but she was urged not to be affected), and a soft gentle voice which never quite seemed to match it. Her home was in Cheyne Walk – 'We often went about by river; in those days the King's Road was a private road, one's coachman had to have a special badge to be allowed to drive along it.' Somehow, aided by her family things were got going again, but Henry Hayter never really recovered heart. I remember him as an indignant and incalculable old man, extremely well read, and insisting upon winning at dominoes. Occasionally he would abruptly ask one 'Who did Anne of Brittany marry?' a thing I have never known although a great deal of European history hinges upon it. Narrowing his malign blue eyes, he would say suddenly, *à propos* of absolutely nothing, 'I hate that beast Brahms.' He had his full quota of Victorian husband selfishness, and went abroad every summer before the crash, cheerfully stravaguing round Europe while my grandmother, who was always having another baby, remained behind. In fact, she liked having babies and disliked travel, so perhaps everyone was happy. As a family they give an over-all impression of being intelligent but rather stuffy. Great-aunt Julia Druce was a kind of Forsyte to end Forsytes, even going so far as to live in the Bayswater Road. She kept a carriage well into the twenties; sitting bolt upright behind two overfed chestnuts she spanked around London, regardless of the dislocation of traffic, long after practically everyone else except the royal family had abandoned this method of transport.

An element of strangeness, an incalculability of event, has a way of filtering through into the most stereotyped families. Catherine Romney, my father's great-grandmother, was born in the West Indies where her father and his father-in-law were both serving with the same regiment. Her mother was not yet twenty, and her grandmother, still a young woman, also gave birth to a daughter at exactly the same time. Some disturbance – the Caribs, a hurricane, or more probably the French, caused the hasty removal of both families directly after the births had taken place. The two babies were put in a large basket together, and when the crisis was over one was found to be dead. No one knew which, but the younger mother was given the benefit of the doubt and allowed to keep the surviving baby. Catherine Romney spent the rest of her days uncertain whether she was her aunt or herself, which must have given life a slightly unanchored and surrealist feeling.

My father's great-uncle, another William Hayter, had got into Winchester as Founder's Kin, because the family traced their descent from William of Wykeham's sister. But by 1882 there were altogether too many Founder's Kin, and this way of entry was abolished. My father got himself a scholarship there, and subsequently to New College where he read Greats and got a second – 'Such a good thing that he didn't get a first,' my mother used to say comfortably, 'or he might have become a don, and that I really *could* not have endured.'

In their tastes my parents were wholly unsuited to one another. My mother's spiritual home was a covered wagon, she would have loved to pioneer, to go out to some distant desert and wrest a hard living out of a disobliging soil. Nor, much as she loved her family, would the absence of social life have troubled her very much. Delicately poised human relationships were not her strong suit. Fate accordingly placed her in the valley of the Nile, where people had been making things grow without appreciable difficulty for the last ten thousand years, obliged to make conversation at dinner parties in halting French to the wives of hyper-sensitive Egyptian ministers. My father was a Londoner, widely travelled, and never happier than when at sea, in a large or small ship. My mother was unable to swim and refused ever to put to sea unless she wanted very much to get to the other side. My father read a book a day. My mother read only Dickens, Scott and Thackeray, Jane Austen, Trollope ('but there's too much politics'), Kipling, Galsworthy, *Punch, The Times,* and the

Bible. My father was extremely gregarious; a keen raconteur, he was prepared to raconte happily in French, German, Italian, Greek, or Arabic. He loved poetry with an absorbed and bone-deep passion; my mother thought it foolishness, and any unfortunate young man who had addressed a sonnet to her had been briskly struck off the list. My father liked to walk, climb, sail, or swim; declined after he was a young man ever again to ride a horse, and shot intermittently and then mainly in self-defence. To him a garden was primarily a place in which one sat in a deck-chair reading Proust or *Blackwood's Magazine* or the Greek Anthology, preferably surrounded by a powerful smell of roses which one drowned out by a still more powerful smell of Turkish cigarettes. To my mother a garden was a place of ceaseless activity; one never *sat down* there, however many people there were to do the work. They were not even politically twinned; he was a Whig and she a Tory. Both were deeply religious and both played golf; these seemed to be their sole meeting grounds. But they were enough. During their nineteen years of married life I never heard a disagreeable word between them, or felt that there could have been one when I was not there. Their happiness was confident and obvious and one rested on it like a cushion.

There was still a long year to wait for marriage until Meg came back from India to take on the care of her father. My father's leave was up in September, and from Egypt he set about giving my mother an idea of how life would be. At times the wait was stultifying. 'Nothing much is happening except the heat,' he wrote from Cairo on June 3rd of 1905, but at the end of the month the court and the government moved to the cooler climate of Alexandria, and things looked up. 'I am having rather an amusing time (for me) in the Ministry, now that I'm in charge. Last year I was quite new to the work, and when I was left in charge I had to let the heads of departments carry on as they liked, more or less: this year I am impressing on them all that everything of any importance must be referred to me. They are all older than I am, some of them much older, and some of the old Frenchmen and Italians are a little restive. I think however that they are now going on all right: I was very polite to them all which pays in these affairs . . . McIlwraith, I see, has become Sir Malcolm, of which I am glad, but I wish they would give Brunyate a C.M.G., which he thoroughly deserves and would like. I don't think I care a bit about these things for myself. I can't really see that it matters except perhaps as an outward and visible sign that you have done good work . . . My latest present – 22 books of devotion! These will be exchanged for works of a more cheerful kind. I can quite understand having and reading sermons or theological treatises on difficult questions, but I don't want to have my religious feelings and emotions laid down for me by anyone else whatever.'

'There is no ceremony down here,' he wrote on July 4th. 'I believe you would like this friendly informal sort of life as much as I do . . . A good deal of excitement here over the conviction of an Egyptian Mudir (Governor of a Province) and a judge of the Mohammedan Religious Court, for forgery: they have been sentenced to two years imprisonment with hard labour a-piece. They are both rich and have bought up the native papers, which are agitating and getting up petitions. The Court that sentenced them was entirely composed of native judges, which is a good thing: it shows they are beginning to have an idea of what justice means: a few years ago no one would have dreamed of punishing a Mudir or a Kadi, whatever he did. The local papers contain some polite references to the incompetent young idiot in charge of the Ministry of Justice: I rather like it.'

On the 7th he is in a more thoughtful mood. 'The only thing I sometimes wonder about is the question of friends. There may be people one of us likes and the other doesn't, which would be awkward; but I hope you will like just a few people here, who have been very good friends to me: I don't care about the rest. The Findlays and the Lindleys are the chief: unfortunately they are both diplomatic and may be moved on at any moment. Findlay is an enormous Scotsman, about 6 ft 6, and is Lord Cromer's second in command: he is not very brilliant, but is extremely sound and has very good judgement, he is the best friend possible, but makes friends very slowly. I don't believe he could do a mean thing if he tried. Mrs Findlay is so good-looking that you might call her beautiful: very kind: laughs a good deal but always good-naturedly: not very clever but sensible, and has as clean a mind as anyone I know. I think she is like you in some ways, but she hasn't got anything like your strength of character. Both of them have been and continue to be extraordinarily kind to me, and are very much prepared to greet you with enthusiasm. Lindley is festive, sensible, amusing and a very good fellow; he was at Winchester with me. Mrs Lindley is a very sensible, rather clever woman: not very good-looking: a sister of Lord Lovat: absolutely no sort of side: very kind and nice to people she likes, but intolerant of flirting married women, people who swagger, and lecturing bores.

'Have I prejudiced you against them with these character sketches? The whole lot of them are not worth your little finger, but they are some of the straightest, kindest, and nicest people I ever met and I much want you to like them.'

On the 11th he is still considering friends and married life in general. 'The Lyons have asked us to stay with them when we first get out. They have a jolly house out in Ghezireh, and I think it would be rather a good plan. He is a fat solid silent sapper: Director General of Surveys, very learned and clever and a very good sort. She is a nice little amusing shrimp of a woman and a great friend of mine . . . This will make you laugh, but I have been watching husbands and wives together ever since I got back to Egypt, and I have come to the conclusion that most husbands don't let their wives alone enough. I don't mean in the way of leaving them to themselves, but in the way of letting them do as they like in small things. I hear men who are quite good fellows pointing out to their wives continually what they ought to do, when it really doesn't matter twopence, also nagging at them when anything goes wrong. Don't let's do this. I want to give you the best possible time for the rest of your life, and if I do rile you without meaning to, just tell me.'

Next week he is back on the local colour. 'Our poor old Grand Mufti, the Sheikh Mohammed Abdou, died the other day: he was a very good old man and rather a friend of mine. He is the chief religious man among the Mohammedans and also the great legal swell in family matters which in Islam are all mixed up with religion. He was most enlightened and was a great reformer, whereby he got himself rather disliked by the high and dry old Mohammedan dignitaries. Findlay and Mitchell-Innes and I walked in his funeral procession through Alexandria and jolly hot it was in a frock coat and a tarboosh. Everyone walks at a Moslem funeral and in any order, so that you see the Prime Minister and a butcher-boy side by side, which I think is a sound scheme for a funeral . . . I am rather bothered by people asking me what I want for a wedding present when I don't in the least know.'

By the 21st his spirits are steadily rising. 'I go for a long swim every morning before breakfast and generally play golf or tennis from 5 to 7, and bridge at the Findlays in the evening. Edward Cecil is staying with them, and Mitchell-Innes here, and we have the best of good times except that you aren't here. Cecil, Machell and Mitchell-Innes have just been having a court of enquiry on my figure, and the decision is that I have got fatter and that you would be quite justified in throwing me over. It is only honest to tell you this but it's a gross libel. What ought I to do about the Dean? You can't tip a Dean, can you? But I should like to give him something.'

The year was at last done; he wrote a final letter from the Hotel Casino, Stan Stefano, Alexandria. 'This is my last letter, as I shall be home before a letter written for the next mail . . . The time has seemed very long but I have not changed in the very least unless it is in the way of loving you more than ever. I always thought, and I still think, that you are miles too good for me, but I believe, all the same, that I can make you happy. I daresay other people may have been as much in love as I am, though it doesn't seem probable to me, but I'm certain no one ever trusted anyone as fully and wholly as I trust you . . . In spite of what you say in your letters I think you may be getting a little nervous about such a great change in your life, but you have nothing to fear: I love you with all my heart.'

III

It *must* sometimes have been raining. Nearly half my early childhood was spent in England, where from time to time at least a light drizzle would certainly have set in. But no single recollection of steaming window panes obtrudes, of walks under dripping elm trees; not so much as an incident connected with mackintoshes or the hasty putting up of motor-car hoods. The usual alchemy of middle age has taken over, and all seems bathed in a perpetual mellow and caressing sunlight. One's shadow leaps before one across the English daisies, falls blue and hard on the dusty footpaths of Zamalek. In a like way all one's friends and neighbours seem, through the haze of time, to have been charming. The names and faces of the boring or disagreeable are blotted out as if they were repented sins. There must have been serpents lurking in the Eden of Gezira; if there were they have disappeared somewhere up inside all those lush flowering trees, jacaranda and golden mohr, among the datura whose huge white bells of flowers hung moveless in the hush of noon or swayed in the hot afternoon winds, trumpets of frozen foam amidst small gnarled branches. (It was said, and not only by Nanny, that the sweet smell of the datura flowers was so strong that if one fell asleep under the tree one would never wake again, but life was too full to have time for this fascinating form of suicide.)

It was true that on the only side of us where we had a next door lived Lady Brunyate, and that Lady Brunyate, who had no children, was inclined to register affrontedness when our rabbits escaped and ate down her petunias, but she was just a disquieting feeling, her face never swung into focus. Equally shadowy, though charming and friendly, were the Ronnie Grahams, who lived opposite. The fact that they had no children made them very slightly disembodied, insubstantial and unreal. Life when one is three can be so preoccupying that there is no time to focus upon faces. Adults were adjuncts of their much more interesting children: were skirts or trousers (and had much better be trousers), conveying an agreeable or disagreeable or sometimes negative message to one's consciousness. Why bother to look up into their faces? To do so is to have to arm oneself with gravity against their gush, with separateness against their intrusion, their boring requests for kisses. Why, because one is under five, should one be traditionally expected to kiss people one scarcely knows, but who happen to feel well disposed towards one's parents and to like one's rose-leaf face? Oh those elderly She's-got-a-great-look-of-Nell relations! Who is Nell, anyway? My looks are mine. Greatly welcome were those who expected nothing, who were not especially interested in one, who paid one the high compliment of living their own rather interesting lives as if one were not there. Love is for Father-and-Mother, Nanny-and-Ena, Mohammed-and-Ahmed, and not for every Tom, Dick, and Harry, though they had a much better chance of it than their female counterparts.

Ned Cecil was a splendidly aloof grown-up, acceptable even if he arrived in the middle of the sacred parental hour in the drawing-room. Coming upon William building a bridge of bricks across a river of polished floor between two Persian rugs he would immediately and silently involve himself in this operation, getting the scheme without having to be told. Building bricks of this epoch invariably came from Germany and included Gothic arches and stained glass windows and a general improving stress upon ecclesiastical architecture, but Ned Cecil rose above this and built a lighthouse with a lighted candle at the top surrounded with stained glass windows, and turned off all the lights and caused us all to be ships in the darkness keeping away from the rocks. As a young man he had, like my father, suddenly become unbearably bored with London. When on guard at Wellington barracks he had asked Kitchener to dinner, filled him up with champagne, and persuaded him to take him on the Sudan campaign as his ADC. From the Egyptian Army Cecil gravitated into a job in the Egyptian Ministry of Finance, and wrote an extremely funny book published after his death, called *The Leisure of an Egyptian Official*, which is now, alas, out of print. The point about him, from our point of view, was that he built lighthouses because he liked building lighthouses, and not to curry favour or put on a child-loving act, and it is a difference of which, at the receiving end, one is immediately aware.

Early childhood holds aching stretches of boredom, as well

as its griping eternities of grief and fear, its spellbinding hours of delight. Its strength lies in its forgetfulness. Sometimes those Nanny-and-May walks seemed endless, day after day, along the glittering Nile in its afternoon breeze-ruffled greenness. Little gusts of dustiness teased one's eyes, ruffled the fringe of the pram canopy. A mile south along the river bank was the bridge to Giza, interestingly called the Pongly-Zongly: it was many years before these words revealed themselves to me as Pont des Anglais. Half-way there, by the race-course entrance, lived the Goschen family with a sweet Danish mother and a father called Teddy who was an unrepentant teaser of them and of everyone else. They were called Jean, Joyce, Alec and Edward, and all were fair and rather square, except Jean, who was very pretty and had an unrealised ambition to become a fast runner. One of the younger ones had a glass eye, and their Nanny made such immense capital out of this fact that an aura of pride and specialness came to envelop the whole family, for of all the weapons in the Nanny-armoury an incurable disability in one of her charges is the most powerful (short of having one of them a royal bridesmaid). Near here too was Dan Barton, serious and freckled, and famous in school for pressing so hard with his pencil that his sums were scored many pages deep. 'Not so *hard*, Dan,' Miss Quibell would entreat, but in mild tones because he was a hard-working character to whom it was impossible to be disagreeable. Further still, beyond the race-course, lived Mary and Pamela Rowlatt, fun to play with, and unique in being allowed to eat the sticky nutty sweets sold by Egyptian street-vendors; their parents both having been brought up in Egypt were less paralysed by germ phobia than most English people, and did not share in Nanny's deep Wesleyan conviction that everything in Egypt was unclean.

We never seemed to get anywhere on our walks. The Pongly-Zongly might at least have had some traffic or camels or something diverting on it. We would simply turn round and go back by the same way. 'It's cooler by the river. Lay hold of the pram handle, dear, while we cross the road.' This was an unnecessary precaution; the roads were empty. Nothing came along but an occasional rattling arabiyeh, a rare carriage, or Colonel Blunt in his dog-cart, a smart syce up behind. The Nile island of Gezira was still pastoral and not yet suburban. Fields held thin tethered donkeys, occasionally accompanied by an enchanting baby donkey covered in milk-white curls. Enormous water buffaloes rolled slowly along the dusty un-macadamized roads and into the snake-grass surrounded fields. Little Egyptian girls, with long pink cotton dresses and gold ear-rings in their small milk-chocolate coloured ears, tended the buffaloes and in loud trenchant tones directed their desultory progress across the waste spaces of the island. Gathering up the buffalo dung as soon as it fell, to be dried and used as fuel, the little girls piled it into baskets with their bare hands and swayed gracefully on, carrying the baskets on their heads.

'Fancy! In their bare hands!' Ena said shockedly to Nanny, unaware that Herodotus too in his day had commented upon this Egyptian peculiarity. 'To think of human people doing that! You'd think they'd learn to make themselves spades.'

Nanny, now in her third winter in Egypt, decided to play this down.

'I'll thank you, William, not to walk just in front of the pram.'

Inland from here lived Rettles and Tony de Cosson, freckled and supremely skilful at turning cartwheels. Tony de Cosson, in addition to other charms, had six toes on his left foot, which he would sometimes display to a few select friends for a small cash consideration. Their stone house was, unlike everyone else's, unplastered, and it had a roofed-in verandah where the whole de Cosson family slept out all the year round. They had curly hair and dark eyes and never made any observations that were not strictly necessary.

Over the way, in a salmon-coloured house, was Clavia Goodman, a gentle and dreamy only child with large grey eyes and a far-away look; her mother was an American and provided specially delicious and nowhere else obtainable snow cakes at tea parties after the dancing class. Here too were three Olympian characters called Hugh, Sandy, and Billy McKillop, who disappeared to prep-schools in England almost before I had time to take in which was which. One of their grandfathers had built all the lighthouses (the real ones) along the Egyptian coast, and the other one, a north country engineer called Sir William Willcocks, had built the Aswan dam.

'Not too far in front now, William dear. And don't lag, Priscilla.'

Across the river on the Giza road passed endless nose-to-tail strings of camels and donkeys, rolling or pattering under heavy bales. The eucalyptus avenue, newly planted, bent sideways in the wind. A felucca, full of round earthenware pots, was making its way slowly upstream. I had a stone in my shoe and nobody seemed to be waiting for me.

If I had my hoopstick I could bang it along the railings and make that striking melancholy sound, a sort of high banging tune. Inside the railings lived the Ronnie Lindsays, and then the Percivals whose name on Egyptian lips was always, confusingly, Burzibulls, there being neither p's nor v's in the Arabic alphabet: Mrs Dallin, too, lived here, and her husband, Mr Dallin, a genial soul who organized all the little boys into playing cricket on a rush-matting pitch, or failing them, the little girls. An otherworldly consecrated look would come over the faces of the fathers teaching their sons to hold a straight bat, the kind of look and the kind of moment at which, in an American film, a distant choir would be heard angelically chanting. Little girls were allowed to swipe happily with their bats all nohow; they were really only there to make up the numbers. How could a bat not be straight? Bats *are* straight; and not even the most shrieking and neglected girl can unstraighten them. Do you mean upright? Well, why not say so? All the same it was intoxicating to make a run, and Mr Dallin was uniformly encouraging and always on one's side over L.B.W.

'Don't lag, Priscilla. I've told you before, dear.'

'Why not, Nanny?'

'Because I say. That's enough.'

My hand in Ena's was sticky and my throat felt dry.

Perhaps, nearer home, we might meet Jock and Donny Liddell, or Ida Knatchbull, whose parents had glamorously died young leaving her in charge of a very prim aunt called Mrs Purvis who minded desperately if anyone spilt jam on the tablecloth. Or Eileen and Mervyn Molesworth, who had black hair and bicycles and a father in the irrigation department, or Hugh Blunt, or Jennifer Trelawney, red-haired and Cornish and the possessor of more plasticine than anyone else on the island. Or the Cheethams, who kept cheetahs in their basement, or so I firmly believed although I had been to tea in their house several times without ever actually seeing any. Why else would they be called Cheethams? But the leboc trees rattled dustily, Zamalek seemed to be empty. Soon there would be milk, and jam sandwiches, and washing one's feet, and putting on an embroidered muslin dress instead of a plain muslin one, and release from the nursery into the infinitely more entertaining and exciting company of one's parents.

'Need we go for a walk, Nanny? Need we?' But it seemed we always needed to.

'We'll go to the Sirdaria Gardens,' Nanny sometimes said, concedingly, 'seeing that the Sirdar is in the Sudan and not there. You make such a noise', she added reprovingly, dampening down any tendency to excitement, 'that I hardly like to take you there to play when he's at home.'

The way to the Sirdaria Gardens lay across the Boulac Road, past the house of Sir Maurice Amos, an uproarious Quaker who liked to sit back to front on one of my mother's Chippendale chairs reading extracts out of *The Rose and the*

Ring (and in due course, *The Young Visiters*), with shouts of delighted laughter, oblivious of whether anyone else was amused or not, and such was the quality of his mirth that they generally were. His son Andrew was a friend and ally of William's and a devoted carrier out of his plans and devices, a silent flaxen-haired figure whose blue linen shorts were always made rather too long for him, but whether on Quaker principles or to allow for growth who could say? He had a sister in a pram and a nursery maid called Beatrix whose name and face are inextricably associated in my mind with beetroot, after which I imagined her to be called, but the family zest for life seemed to be concentrated in Sir Maurice who laughed with a kind of blazing relish, a total loose-limbed abandon that caused the chair-back to crack and bits of loose plaster to float down off the ceiling.

In Nanny's company I felt as she felt about the Egyptians, and was far from being a little friend of all the world. She had disapproving views about the Egyptians, all of whom, except indoor servants and a particular arabiyeh driver called Shemps, came under her suspicion or scorn. To her, they were primarily the people who had oppressed the children of Israel. She came, in time, to regard rather more of them with a cautious tolerance, but in the main insularity prevailed and they seemed to her a sly and unreliable bunch. Although she stayed single, marriage was an occupational risk amongst English nannies and nursery maids in Cairo; they were besieged by eligible bachelors and the wastage was extremely high. Even the velvet bonnet and bonnet strings of William's first nurse had proved an insufficient protection; she was swept off, after a two-year siege, by a very clever engineer called Mr Jackson, confused in our minds with the toad intruder in *The Tale of Mrs Tittlemouse*. Under-nurses were objects of steady pursuit by lance-corporals, sergeants, and even occasionally by frantic second lieutenants. Ena succeeded May, was succeeded in her turn by Mary West, Annie MacNicol, and Rose Hunt, and somewhere in between there was also a Lucy and a Maud. Almost all were united in taking a low view of the Egyptians, and I held tight to the pram when we crossed the Boulac Road, which, once the Zamalek bridge was completed and opened, led across our island of Gezira and over the Boulac bridge into the heart of Cairo. On the other side of the Zamalek bridge, a mile or so north down the river, lay the wicked city of Em-baba. Along the Boulac Road a ceaseless stream of people from Em-baba poured into Cairo. They seemed mysteriously always to be going across the island into Cairo and never to be coming out, as if Cairo were a great mouth that swallowed them up. There were flat carts with vegetables and sugar-cane, long-robed men shouting incessantly at over-burdened donkeys, men with rolling hashish-loaded eyes, men chewing sugar-cane and spitting out the pith, loud-voiced, black-eyed, and looking at Nanny and Ena in a way that Nanny and Ena visibly did not like. There were men in burnouses, and little boys in cotton skull-caps, and men in tarbooshes, men in bare feet and stiff unbleached cotton robes, and men in bright yellow leather slippers and silk robes, and women endlessly and eternally dressed in rusty black, veiled and garrulous and resigned. Across their shoulders they carried babies, their nodding shiny little faces black with crawling flies.

'You wouldn't think they could breathe, poor mites,' Nanny said. 'They say it's a part of their religion', she told Ena, 'not to wash boy babies till they are two years old. Girls, now, they don't trouble about, either way.'

'It's grievous,' Ena said, and I drew down a disapproving upper lip in sympathy. We hurried across the Boulac Road and never under any pretext went down it. Nanny-and-May, or Nanny-and-Ena, once they had got over being shocked, preferred not to notice what went on. The Boulac Road was a place where people cursed and shouted and incessantly called upon God to witness their wrongs; when not spitting out chewed sugar-cane they spat out spit, they wiped their noses unashamedly on the back of their hands or held their noses and blew them into the dust and shook their heads free, they greeted one another across great distances in tones of untrammelled pleasure or dislike, they pissed or squatted as need arose in wide open spaces, they begged unceasingly in high whining desperate voices which they switched off without difficulty when greeting an acquaintance in the same line of business.

'Why can they do it, Nanny, and not us?'

'They're heathens.'

'Father says they aren't heathens,' William pointed out.

'Well then, don't ask me, dear. We must suppose they know no better.'

It was a moment of relief when the iron gates of the Sirdaria clanged tight. Even inside this stone-walled haven which lay along the Boulac Road one did not feel too secure. The harsh incessant shouting floated over, the braying of donkeys rising to fever pitch, the rattle of the flat carts, their drivers shouting comments, yelling Oh-ah! Oh-ah! Oh-ah riglac! and people on foot complaining passionately at being hustled off the road. The gardens themselves were large and empty of people and full of possibilities. There were groves of poinsettias with their strange thick red flowers that were the same shape as their leaves, and of orange trees, heavy with ripe fruit, and blossom, and small hard green oranges, all at the same time. In a corner under the high wall, away from Nanny and the pram, there was a fine hidden place in which to be secret, in which to enter a world unorganised by grown-ups. We retired into a domestic bliss of mud-cakes and leaf plates and piles of berries for fruit. Here, uninterrupted, William and I could make and be busy, thickening out the hibiscus walls with palm branches and eucalyptus boughs, at peace and very muddy in a dim, green, shuttered world. The lizards and the grass-hoppers and the large burnt-sienna butterflies and the hornets were all shut out.

Suddenly from behind the stone wall came the unmistakable loud blood-curdling roar of a lion. Starting low and growlingly, it rose to a throbbing rage, sank again, gave to our thudding hearts the hope that the peril had passed. We had heard lions often enough in the Giza Zoo before feeding time. Sounding still nearer, the roar rose again to a crescendo of fury. Any minute now the lion would leap over the wall and devour us. We faced each other, panic-stricken amongst the poinsettias. For a full moment we stood with our mouths open in a suffocating fear, before we found courage even for flight. We fled past the orange trees and the little channels that watered the petunia beds, over the grass and under the date palms to where Nanny was knitting in inexplicable calm beside the pram, and cast ourselves into the shelter of that starched and lifebuoy-soaped embrace.

'There,' Nanny said, 'to think of you both being so silly, and you a great boy nearly seven, William!'

'Not till August,' William gulped, factual in the teeth of woe.

'Fancying it was a lion! The very idea. It's only a camel you heard, roaring in the Boulac Road. Whatever made you take such a thing in your head? Surely to goodness you know what an angry camel sounds like by now?'

Sobered, we walked home shufflingly to tea. Along the Boulac Road yet another funeral would be winding with sad sounds from hurrying bare-foot mourners, and, too often, a baby-sized coffin.

'Nanny, what happens to the Egyptian babies when they die?'

'In my Father's house', Nanny said crisply, 'are many mansions. Come here to me, William, whatever's happened to your tie?'

Afternoon lay heavy on us, the kites wheeled high in the remote blue sky. I felt the blankness and lowness that comes after a fright. The funeral tramped slowly by. Three or four came past daily from Em-baba the wicked city, where the mortality rate must have been extremely high. Mourners, real or hired professionals, walked the long road across Gezira and through Cairo to the burial grounds in the Mocattam hills, where the bodies could not pollute the Nile, sole source of water-supply. A distant huddle of brown houses built of mud, Em-baba was forbidden ground, even for Mohammed, for Ahmed and Abdu. No one explained the nature of its wickedness, and its name was confusing. I imagined an indefinite multiplication of the Forty Thieves, an entire population who spent their time putting each other into jars and filling them up with boiling oil. Even the trams that went to Em-baba were different from the Giza and the Pyramid trams, being open-sided and all third class. Em-baba it seemed was poor as well as wicked, no one there ever went first or second class. Behind the Em-baba trams their trailers swung out, packed with people, always a quota of unfortunates going into Cairo to expose their deformities for begging. Em-baba was so wicked that no one could even beg there. Laden with forty or more thieves, the trams came trundling over the Zamalek bridge with a pleasant groaning sound. The bridge was only a quarter of a mile away across gardens, one heard the trams as one lay in bed at noon resting, or under the mosquito net at night; the light flashed in as they passed. Every morning and afternoon the middle part of the bridge swung open sideways and stayed open for an hour, thus halting the flow of people from Em-baba and places north, and giving passage to huge heavily laden swan-like feluccas, full of bales, or pots, or sacks of earth, or corn or melons. The Zamalek bridge was *the* bridge, our bridge, its rhythm as settled and reliable as dawn or dusk, the level scream of its opening as regular as the noon gun from the Citadel, or the striking of the cuckoo clock.

Away from Nanny and Ena, and in the company of my parents, I felt quite differently about the Egyptians, and the Boulac Road held no terrors, except for the blind men, with their sticks tapping and their white sightless eyes staring. This confidence may have been partly because in the company of my parents I was generally driving and not walking. But certainly reassurance flowed from my father's liking for the Egyptians, and because it never would have occurred to him to be frightened of them. He spoke good Arabic, and in his presence ruffled Egyptians became unruffled, and the most complicated situations seemed to disentangle themselves. My mother's Arabic was halting and intermittent, but she too seemed able to cope, out of the general fearlessness and Christianity of her personality. My father, in what seemed to me a wholly unnecessary way, was always talking to Egyptians, answering their greetings, thanking them for blessings, questioning them, having jokes with them, engaging in long conversations with total strangers met with on the roads or fields. Useless to leap up and down in the dust, tugging his hand like a fish on a line; on he went, listening and talking and listening and talking, as if we had all day. The time that grown-ups waste in conversation with one another puts a stern strain on the most devoted affection.

There were days of brightness when Nanny could be persuaded to take us to the Swings. Too much of the Swings was, she considered, over-exciting. Besides, there were rough children there. They shot by one, delectable beings of eleven or even twelve years old, wearing brightly coloured clothes, playing tearing around and jostling games, shouting at one another in strange tongues, French, Greek, Syrian, or still more strange English. There were older friends of ours, girls with swinging plaits, Jean Westropp or Mary Madden, whirling round the giant stride with careless expertise, there were the McKillops and John Stansfeld, sending the swings so high that you wondered they didn't all go right over the top, there were stranger boys from Cairo, with sticking-up hair and knobbly knees, rushing up the palm trees and sliding down the summer-house roof. There were seven-year-old Egyptian boys, sons of pashas, just out of the harem and into the world of men, and cocky as bantams with it. There were mulberry trees and apricot trees and lashings of sand and a hard tennis court permanently occupied by Copts with long archaic faces accusing each other of cheating in high despairing accents. The whole of the Sporting Club was much more fun than anywhere else except the Pyramids or the Zoo, both well outside pram range, and the Swings was the crown and summit of it.

'Can't we go to the Swings, Nanny? Can't we go?'

'Those that don't ask often get.'

'Not the dull old New Gardens,' William said. 'Not the Grotto.'

'No,' I echoed, 'not the Grotto.'

The Grotto was an artificial mountain with tunnels, arched over paths, dark corners and rocky hollows and pools and other delights, but it contained also an aquarium with a great big Nile catfish with huge wavering whiskers, which sent shivers down my spine. It was the haunt of nuns leading queues of orphans in check dresses, walking two by two and whispering to each other in a subdued and browbeaten way. Built by a rich pasha for the pleasure of a favourite wife and turned into a public garden approached through a turnstile, it was also the stamping ground of Orthodox priests with beards and upside down top hats, of monks in rough robes and sandals, of Roman Catholic priests with drowsy Italian voices and hot black soutanes smelling of garlic.

'Priests indeed,' Nanny would say aside to Ena, with a firm Wesleyan equation between holiness and soap. 'Their smell!'

'And the way they look at you,' Ena agreed. 'Not my notion of the clergy.'

The Grotto was not without charm. The pines on the summit of its artificial hill rustled fascinatingly, and its pools were perfect for sailing paper boats made out of folded copies of *The Times* or the *Egyptian Gazette*. But on the whole it was a babyish prammy place and had nothing in it to compare with the Swings.

'Can't I come on too?' I demanded, one hot afternoon in the Swings, in the autumn of 1912. William and Eileen Molesworth, playing with some splendidly rough children, were on one end of the see-saw, waiting for the rough children to get themselves adjusted at the opposing end.

'No. You're too little.'

'I'm not little.'

'Anyway there isn't room.'

Away they went, up with a sickening jerk, down with a jarring bump. The rough children, much older and heavier, were getting into their stride. 'Ully! Ully!' they kept saying in their uncouth tongue. I stood back against a palm tree, defiantly biding my time. Each jerk at the summit was higher and wilder, each descent more abrupt and tooth-rattling. You could see William and Eileen becoming aware of having more than met their match, but they hung gamely on. Eileen's long black hair came down with a thud on her shoulders at each landing. Her linen smock was crumpled. One of the rough children was a French boy with very short shorts of the kind deprecated by the English; he kept uttering unintelligible cries in a derisive voice. Near the cricket ground, behind the oleanders, Nanny and Ella were putting out our picnic tea things. The rough children brought down their end of the see-saw with a really triumphant bump and William and Eileen were catapulted from the high end and shot through the air, landing on the grass some way away with a monumental thud. As they fell, Eileen's boot struck William on the temple. She lay in a heap slightly on top of him; her linen smock was up round her neck revealing a petticoat with a broderie anglaise frill. In a minute she was up, bumped and crying, but William lay quite still.

The whole scene was interesting rather than moving. It

never occurred to me that he might be dead. It did however so occur to Nanny. On the instant she was there; her face white at first, and then very red. William opened his eyes and moved and she felt him all over and picked him up, and the Molesworth Nanny came up and said, 'I never did – those wicked children!' but Nanny seemed bereft of speech. William was very white and seemed not to be able to cry, or even to protest against the hideous indignity of being wheeled home in the pram.

'I never had my turn on the see-saw, Nanny. I never had my turn,' I pointed out, as we hastened home. 'Oh be quiet, do,' Nanny begged. 'Don't let me hear you talk of going on that thing again.'

'But why, Nanny? It was William who fell off.'

'Fell off! Pitchforked off more likely. And a lot you seem to care. Thinking only of your pleasure.'

'It was my turn after him. Why couldn't I have it?'

'Because I say, dear. And that's enough, once and for all.'

'But it isn't fair.'

'Of course not,' Nanny said, with unexpected frankness. 'Why should it be? Hurry up, now, for any sake.'

William was concussed and sick and went to bed for a few days and then appeared completely to get over it, but Nanny never did, and it was our last day for many years at the delectable Swings.

In the autumn of 1911, when I was just three, William and I spent a whole November day with neighbours, unaccompanied either by Nanny or by May. In the evening my father came to fetch us home himself, and this too was unusual. As we walked the short distance home under the avenues of leboc trees, through the alternating pools of darkness and splashes of bright light, something of his relief and exultation communicated itself to me along the hand I held. Outside our front gate I was aware, for the first time, of the miraculous clarity of the Egyptian night, a blazing canopy that seemed to hold more stars than sky. There was, William and I were told, a surprise awaiting us. In the house we were met by the long faces of the servants, and the sympathetic gloom with which Moslems react to the birth of a female child, nine good months wasted on the production of the wrong model. Mohammed trod softly, his Nubian pride abated. To be a youngest or an only child is to miss a pithy experience. Never to know that lighted room at evening, that round new head in the crook of one's mother's arm, that sharp assault of astonishment, delight, and apprehension, is to lose a major moment. Powerful sensations chase each other round one's inside – this is rich – our numbers are swelled – this is comfortable, boastable about – but how will it affect *me*? Parents too are so obviously delighted, so conscious of their monumental cleverness and luck that it is impossible not to feel swept along in the tide of their thankfulness and triumph. But aren't they perhaps *too* pleased about something that isn't me?

After this my mother, in spite of the Slessor constitution, was quite ill. She was prescribed a diet of raw meat chopped up in a saucer, by her doctor, Bonté Elgood, who was Maurice Amos's sister. She disliked it very much indeed and fed it to the birds, or failing them, to William and to me. Work on the Zamalek bridge, then being built, was suspended for ten days lest the noise should disturb her, and this now seems surprising. The several thousand inhabitants of Em-baba continued to ferry themselves and their dead across the Nile, but as they had been doing this for some millenniums it perhaps worried them less than it might have done.

IV

Life in 1910 has no sooner done surprising us by its similarity
to life in 1964 than it startles us by sounding Georgian, if not
medieval. Writing to my mother during their long annual
summer separation, when she took us for coolness to England,
my father's words and phrases could almost have been written
yesterday. He will see about the creeper on the south wall,
about the re-establishment of the long bed of phloxes. Teddy
Goschen has carried out a successful teasing of the German
Chargé d'Affaires. He has spent the day at Helouan with the
McKillops and played two rounds of golf. 'No!' he says on
August 12th, writing from Zamalek, 'I had nothing to do with
the twins of the wife of the Headmaster of Harrow! Shocking
suggestion: it was the wife of the Headmaster of Rugby I
admired anyhow . . . I am glad to see Robert Scott Kerr has
got the Grenadier Guards. They say the 1st Batt is coming out
here in the spring to relieve the Coldstream . . . Our prize cen-
taureas came out with ragged dirty-white flowers like an aster
suffering from pip . . . The story of the boy Archer-Shee quite
beats me altogether. What becomes of the evidence of the
postmistress? However, I suppose it's all right: I wasn't there,
so I can't judge. I see young Stuart got a 2nd in Greats, which
is the degree taken by all really great men . . . Here's a month

gone, *hamd l'illah*, and only 2½ to go.' 'I have knocked off whiskey at night and have had no stomach troubles since. I expect the Prophet was right and whisky and wine are bad for you in these countries, anyway I feel much better without it.' 'Just met Jackson from the Sudan,' he writes on the 28th from the Turf Club, in Cairo, 'who used to be a great friend of mine. He said, "I hear you have the two prize children in Cairo." So you see,' my father added, with the fatuousness which still sometimes characterizes parents when privately discussing their children, 'the fame of William and Priscilla is spreading over Africa.'

On July 27th we are back in another world. 'The Khedive is having the hell of a time with his family at Constantinople. The Grand Cadi (Sheikh-el-Islam) absolutely refuses to recognize the ex-Countess, his new wife, unless she will appear before the Cadi and publicly repent of her sins and swear on the Koran to lead a clean life. She is treated in Turkey simply as a concubine. The Khedive Mère has announced that if he brings her back to Egypt she will make an open scandal. He is ruining himself all round over this woman who came off the streets of Vienna and was married by an old count in his dotage. She then picked up H.H. and has stuck to him like a burr ever since. He knows what a bad 'un she is, but he is infatuated and can't get rid of her. She used to dress up as a boy and pervade the Palace at Koubbeh under the name of Ali Bey. Selim has cut down the trees we marked: I think it's a great improvement. He has also done away with the long narrow bed of carnations and made the border behind much wider. One young gentleman (English) got mixed up with a Pasha's wife, and had to go to Paris with the Pasha and fight a duel with swords, in which he was run through the shoulder. Don't talk of this.' 'I hear that H.H. recently heard that one of the palace servants was very ill in his native village, so he wrote at once to the local Mamour to go to the village and get the man's livery as H.H. feared it might be damaged if the man was allowed to die in it.' 'They say Ronald Graham is now by far the most popular man in the country. This result he has achieved by ruling every native he has come across with a rod of iron. He sends Ministers and Governors on errands and gives them the sharpest wiggings if they don't do their jobs properly and they all love him for it.' 'We are taking elaborate precautions against cholera, which seems to be spreading round the Black Sea and the Mediterranean. There's no sign of it here at present: but one can't be too careful. In 1902 an old Sheikh coming back from the Pilgrimage brought with him a bottle of water from the sacred well, Zem-Zem, at Mecca: he knew the quarantine people would stop it, so he got a sailor to keep it for him when he went into the quarantine enclosure at Tor, and got it back again when he came out. When he got back to his native village, everyone wanted a drink for his soul's health. To satisfy as many as possible, he poured it into the village well, which it infected, and thereby caused, in the end, several thousands of deaths. If it comes this year it won't last long; the first cool weather generally ends it, and the bad epidemics here are those that start in May or June.'

Sometimes the old recurrent crusade crops up.

'We have been rather near a serious row here, owing to the folly of an American missionary, who has published a paper in Arabic abusing the prophet Mohammed in the most violent way. Quite apart from political reasons I think this is very wrong especially as no Moslem ever mentions the name of Christ without adding, 'upon him be all praise and peace', just as they do for Mohammed and for no one else. I think the whole business is now settled, the missionary withdrawing the article and undertaking not to publish the paper for 3 months. Bell, the acting U.S. consul general, has behaved very well. The whole business is being kept very dark, so don't discuss it with anyone. We don't want either a Moslem riot or a missionary campaign.'

Most of the time we are in the timeless middle east that belongs to no century. 'Abdou is quite confident that he will be a beautiful cook. He also said, with a very large grin, that his various enterprises bring him in a good bit more than his wages so he wouldn't have to make a bit out of the housekeeping.' 'Things here are very quiet indeed; everyone seems to have gone to sleep. The Sheikh Shawish has been sent to prison again and nobody cares either way.' This was August. 'Did I tell you', he wrote on the 17th, 'how Cecil and I had agreed to defy the powers that be, and risk our jobs over the Damietta Salines business? We sent notes home to Gorst and Harvey, who had pretty well agreed to an arrangement in which H.H. and the Prime Minister were interested, and in our notes we explained that the whole thing was a swindle, and we would have nothing to do with it. And now we have got letters from both of them agreeing to drop the scheme – Hoorah! At a meeting of the Council of Ministers the other day the Prime Minister proposed a grant of £50 out of Govt funds for an old official, who had exchanged his pension for money down and then blued all the cash. Cecil refused to allow it, as against the rules. "What," said Mohammed Said, 'have you no pity for this poor old man?" Cecil replied, "Certainly I have. Let us raise the £50 between us out of our own pockets. Here's £5," and produced five sovereigns. As the U.S.S. had given £5, the Ministers, groaning, had to give £10; as they gave £10, the Prime Minister, almost weeping, had to give £20. Cecil says they'll never forgive him till the end of time.'

'All native society is convulsed', he wrote, on September 18th, 'over a ridiculous incident that happened at Alexandria the other day. One Chilli Bey, a nationalist advocate and journalist, went to the govt offices at Alexandria on the Coptic New Year's Day, which was being kept as a fast by the Copts in memory of poor old Boutros. Chilli Bey went into the room of Neguib Pasha Ghali, old Boutros' son, who is now U.S.S. for Foreign Affairs, without being announced, and wished him the compliments of the season. Neguib told him to get out, regarding his visit as an intentional insult (which I believe it was). Chini refused, and sat down. Thereupon Neguib rang for two shawishes, and told them to throw Chilli out, which they did. Chini went away weeping, and the Nationalist papers are screaming for Neguib's blood. You've no idea of the row, the papers are full of it, day after day.' 'I have done for myself!' he had written a fortnight earlier. 'The Ministers all claimed that the new pension law gave them certain special privileges on retiring and requested the Ministry of Finance to take note. I have just written pointing out gently but firmly that their excellencies are quite wrong and are treated under the law just like other officials. I hear they are snorting with fury. I thought of adding a P.S. that my opinion could only be changed if I got a rise of pay of at least £200, but that would hardly have been playing the game properly, which is to convey such things gently by way of Mohammed Said's brother's sister-in-law's second suffragi.' . . . 'Last Sunday in Church I had to stop and laugh in the middle of the hymn, because the line "weary souls, by thousands meekly *stealing*" so exactly describes the Egyptian clerks and minor officials.'

Two strands of feeling run throughout the letters, family affection, and concern for the success of the cotton crop. At the beginning of August he believed the crop to be very promising indeed, and prices were still high. A week later the weather was 'perfectly beastly, N.E. winds and temperatures over 100 every day. But the hot weather was badly wanted for the cotton, which now promises exceedingly well. A good crop would bring at present prices something like 30 million pounds into the country and would solve a lot of difficulties.' By the end of August it was 'still very promising, it has defeated all its numerous enemies except the boll-worm, which will come on now if at all. There are no signs of it yet, and in another week or two we ought to be out of the wood. Ramadan starts in a week and the first Bairam before you get back.' By the 11th all is well, and 'the Sudan cotton crop is excellent too, and they are exporting a great deal over the Red Sea Railway.'

Relieved of this preoccupation he had now only to wait another fortnight for his wife's return. 'Five years today since our wedding,' he had written on August 10th. 'That was the best thing I ever did for myself . . . I don't want you different in any way.' 'Who was the idiot', he asked in July, 'who said that fathers had no natural affection for their children? There isn't a day that I don't feel the need of all three of you. A beast of a week, 102 to 106 every day and very damp. You could hardly get a cigarette to light . . . I always feel so sorry for married couples without children, specially the wives. I wish we lived at home and had six.'

By the 30th September things were really looking up. 'The thought of having you back here seems too good to be true, and to think of waking up in the morning and finding you alongside . . . and then the children coming in and climbing all over us. It really is almost worth while being separated from you all, to have the happiness of getting you back. The time that comes back to me most often when I think of you is that time when I got back, just after William was born, and ran upstairs and hunted for you and heard you call me in rather a weak voice. It was such a tremendous happiness to get back and find you all right, with that fine little baby. Things haven't always gone well for me here these last few years, but you have very much more than made up for everything. So long as I have you and the little things it doesn't really much matter what happens. And if we have a change for the better here, as I think we very likely shall, I shall have nothing left to ask for. (Except', he added irrepressibly, 'to get a little steadier with my drive. I beat Cecil 2 and 1 yesterday.)'

V

When John Henry Slessor died in 1912 his six children were in five different continents, one of which luckily happened to be Europe. The handy one was, inevitably, my mother. (I had been born in Oxford in the autumn of 1908, where she had been succouring his second widowerhood.) His death, as so often happens, caused his family to coalesce even more firmly than before. For the summers of 1912 and 1913 the Slessor sisters took Compton Manor, near Winchester, and here our fathers joined us on their intermittent leaves, taking away their wives for a spell and then returning to address themselves to the rather more arduous task of getting to know their children, who, preferring to play with the others, never seemed over-anxious to be got to be known. A long low brick wall to the south separated the garden from what was then a grassy lane. On this we sat, on those flawless summer evenings that are such an inexplicable feature of early childhood, a quantity of stout-legged cousins in starched linen, consuming strawberries and cream out of saucers. The brick was rubbed and comfortable in the pits of one's knees, the strawberries were large and shiny and local, the grassy lane wandered away under a railway bridge into the allurements of the water meadows. Once, excitingly, an aeroplane passed slowly overhead – 'Look, children, a flying machine!' Summoned by William, the whole household came pelting out in a rattle of long starched aprons to see this wonder. Uncle Andrew, obliged during his leaves to descend from his horse and lay aside his sash and turban, had bought himself a new motor car, in which he sat very high, wearing goggles and a special motoring cap and long coat. Aunt Meg accompanied him on his drives, in the usual motoring veil and tussore dust-coat, uttering, not without cause, little gasps of horror, and clasping the customary half-brick to whip out and prop up the back wheels when gears were missed on hills.

In the mornings we dug indefatigably for gold among the roots of the lime trees.

'How much', Hamer asked, 'shall we find?'

'A heap of treasure,' William told us, 'about a sub-marineful.' He spoke in a carelessly authoritative manner and we never doubted him. Hamer, Peggy Barnard, and I were all struck into silence by the overwhelming sophistication of this reply. Occasionally we came upon a red root which caused a spasm of hope, but on the whole it must have been a frustrating ploy, after a week or so, and the possible cause of a searing incident over the breaking of someone's robin's egg. Practically everyone, except for once, me, was convicted of the crime known in Nanny circles as acting a lie. There is something beautiful and glowing about a watertight alibi, even when one is four, and on this occasion I had been taken for the day by May to visit her married sister in Itchen Abbas, a village that has been, for me, wreathed in roses ever since. Wonderful to be for once outside the grim circle of serious Nanny faces and mutinous infant ones stubbornly pushing out their lower lips and refusing to admit guilt. 'Daisy, Daisy,' I sang light-heartedly and away off key.

This summer, from the high garden wall of a house in Southgate Street, we saw King George and Queen Mary on their quincentenary celebration visit to Winchester College, dressed respectively in frock-coat and top-hat and in strawberry-ice pink moiré silk, and experienced the usual shock of amazement at finding they were not arrayed like the King and Queen of Hearts in Randolph Caldecott's nursery rhyme illustrations. Some of the magic was however conveyed to us through the suspense and excitement of the crowd waiting on the pavement below the wall, and for years afterwards one could go on saying, 'I saw the King and Queen, I saw them,' and be sure of holding one's audience, be sure of the definite black and pink picture in one's mind.

Compton was a pleasant red-brick house with a white-painted door, in a charming setting. A variegated holly tree in the middle of the lawn was useful as fort, home, or hiding-place. There were spreading meadows with oak trees, over which we were led by a daily governess, diligently persuading us to take an interest in nature. The London and South Western Railway clanked merrily past nearby; we needed no persuading to take an interest in this. Everyone had their favourite railway, Hamer was a G.W.R. addict, and William, no doubt for equally sound technical reasons, a staunch supporter of the L. & S.W.R., whilst I, for the sentimental lure of its beautiful blue engines and crimson coaches, was a dedicated fan of the Caledonian.

Through evenings which now seem to have been endlessly golden we walked through the water meadows on the railway's further side, among clear streams and their waving weeds, accompanied by not less than two duty parents. At three and four years old one is always vainly striving to keep up with the longer legs of five-, six-, or seven-year-olds, stumping hopefully along in pursuit of more agile characters who simply never wait. Sometimes it becomes suddenly too difficult, one trails disconsolately behind, a victim of the cheerful unconscious ruthlessness that sets in whenever the children of more than one family are together, a sharp upward curve of effort and accomplishment sending the weaker to the wall. On one such an evening I was carried home on his shoulders by my uncle, Harold Stansfeld. He was a passionate naturalist, and life in India had not dulled his appetite for the English scene. At intervals we stooped to look at things among the mimulus fringes of the rivers, peering down among the waving weeds and the clear gravelly beds for things which he could see and I could not. It must have been tiresome for him, wearing a four-year-old like a fur collar round his neck, but he went on living his life unperturbed and I went on holding on by his ears and hair. A feeling of kindness and safety conveyed itself to me through hands securely grasping my legs. The voices of the others sounded faint and far away but I no longer troubled. I was much higher up than any of them and no further effort was required of me. Riding high, I passed under the railway bridge and down the lane towards home, triumphing over the others who hardly arrived before us. Hamer gave me an old-fashioned look; after all, whose father was it? All very well to neglect them oneself, but when someone else took them up, that was another thing.

It was perhaps this uncle's last walk with his wife among the meadows. He went back to his regiment in India, and was presently sent to France and killed in the battle of Loos in September 1915. We were standing on the doorstep when the telegram came, in London? in Portsmouth? Departure for Egypt was imminent and my mother was taking me to the dentist. Her brother had gone to tell the news to her bereft sister, Aunt Bay was already there; so she continued to take me to the dentist. As we sat in his waiting-room, I saw that the tears were streaming and pouring down her face as if they could never stop. Unchecked, unmopped, they fell with the steady persistence of rain, sinking right into the dentist's carpet. There was this to be said for her, my mother did not sob or gulp, and her face remained uncrumpled. But this manifestation was shocking to me; I regarded her with unconcealed disapproval. Don't cry, they were always saying, and now this! Of all people, one's mother! 'Uncle Harold killed,' I recorded in my diary, in a firm, pothooky, seven-year-old hand. 'Awful fuss.' I could hardly have liked him more.

August took us to rooms by the sea, at Sidmouth, in south Devon, an enchanting little town with which we had a family connection. My mother's Slessor grandfather and great-grand-father had owned Sidmouth Manor, having bought it a couple of generations after they left Scotland. The Slessors too as children had played on Sidmouth's pebbly beach and known the fisherman families of Woolley and Dagworthy, had shrimped among the brick-red rocks below Jacob's Ladder. My grandfather could remember the cottage on the rocks that was there before the sea encroached. As a young man he had lost a signet ring there with his crest on it, and refound it among the rocks, miraculously, many years later. In my mother's childhood convention had forbidden families to bathe together; she and her sisters were shepherded into a bathing machine and left in charge of a bathing woman who towed them, gasping, on the end of a rope from the stern of a rowing boat, which was so disconcerting that they never learned to swim. Their father and brothers swam distantly from another part of the beach. Sea-bathing in the 1870s was a pleasure confined to the well-to-do. Others, with sterling common sense, eschewed the plunge into the cold wet stuff. 'Mere idle bravery, I calls it, with neither mirth nor comfort in it,' the Woolleys opined.

Salcombe and Peak, the twin enclosing cliffs of Sidmouth, were beautiful, dramatic and seemingly sky-high. To boat picnics at Ladrum Bay or Branscombe we were slowly and peacefully rowed by Bob and Tom Woolley through timeless afternoons under the sheer reflected red cliffs. Long ribbons of seaweed undulated below the cool mackerel-haunted seas, whose tidal flow seemed to me, then and since, far more delectable in its changing greys and greens and shadowy hyacinth colours, its alternating deeps and shallows, than the monotonous blue champagne of the Mediterranean. There were shrimps and prawns in plenty in the rocks below High Peak, endless clear tide-washed pools of limpets, anemones and grass-green weed. Sometimes even lobsters were to be caught by such Olympian figures, such prodigies of expertise as Jack, Rodney, and Tony Slessor. The tall red cliff gave back our solitary voices; there was never anyone else there, we might have been in New Zealand. The kingdom of the fore-shore was all ours. The sky was empty, and the sea, except for the horizon silhouette of an occasional dreadnought. There was nothing to hear except sea-gulls and the gentle continu-ous falling of the waves. The sand underfoot was cold and hard and ocean-washed. Winds blew from the west with Atlantic freshness. It could hardly have been less like Egypt.

Outside Marine Place the waves fell on a shingly beach just across the road; a good storm would, with luck, bring pebbles right on to the grassed front garden, where sea-gulls swooped for crusts, and where, brought together for a rare moment of time in the same country the summer before, my grandfather was photographed with his two sons and four grandsons.

'Why not us?' William and Hamer indignantly protested. 'We are boys too.'

'But not Slessors,' Rodney told them. He had a long curly mouth that went up derisively at the corners when he grinned. He was a person on whose side in any game of skill or chance or in any argument it was best to be, in whose company life became at once more dangerous and more fun. He had very fair hair, of the straight and floppy kind, and was wearing his first grey flannel Sunday suit; it was clear that he thought the whole thing of being photographed with a large square Kodak was pretty silly, an aunt-whim. Jack was older, at his public school, he looked very grown-up, serious, and formidable. Tony was still in the stage of linen tunics with large round flat white collars, but he too seemed so old as to be of another generation. He led a precarious existence in which he was alternately tormented and swept along into perilous enterprises; obliged to live dangerously and rather beyond his means he found an admirable ally in his sister Betty with whom at least in term time he could be his age. Silent, long-legged, and seemingly impervious, Tony reacted with spirit, but occasionally took things out on William and Hamer, who were two or three years younger. Betty, learning in a tough school, had to watch her dolls like a hawk to prevent their being swept away by Jack and Rodney and buried with full military honours in the orchard. Two darling boys, loved and cherished, blue-eyed and adept, they had in younger days occasionally expressed themselves by going into the potting shed and breaking up two or three hundred flower-pots with a sledge-hammer. This exorcism of the demon of destruction which must have seemed tiresome at the time paid a handsome dividend in 1944 when Jack was almost solely responsible for preventing the American Army Air Force from bombing the city of Florence into rubble. A safe gulf of years separated me from these lordly beings, who would fortunately

have scorned to pull the hair or steal the dolls of one so irre-
deemably young as I was.

William and Hamer looked crestfallen, and I looked
pleased. Those enviable shorts, that enviable short untangly
hair were not, apparently, a passport everywhere.

My fourth birthday came and went at Sidmouth and was
stormy as to weather but brought with it a doll's tea-set with
mottoes on it and a stuffed toy lion which instantly became a
prototype. Sometimes it was me; another, braver, kinder, self;
more often a trusted bodyguard in a world full of other dangerous animals. I abandoned the blue collar box in favour of
this obviously live being, an untemperamental and solid companion in a world which seemed to spend so much of its
time in rushing past railway carriage windows that I sometimes had the feeling of having been born and brought up in
a wagon-lit.

Train journeys had a spacious, comfortable quality. Trains
went no less fast than they do now, perhaps faster, because
there seemed so little need for fuel economy; but appeared to
stop longer in stations. To travel abroad at all was in itself,
before 1914, a privileged thing. We were accompanied everywhere by cohorts of porters, and as often as not by the
stationmaster, discussing the political situation with my father
in rapid and melancholy French. There was always a perfect
certainty that the train would wait, and I have suffered ever
since from an excess of train calm.

Sea voyages merged into one another. Life on board ship
had a dream-like, always-afternoon quality. It was still divert-

ing, offered renewed opportunity for pleasing forms of sabotage. Soup on colder days, ice-cream on warmer ones, would be served on deck at mid-mornings, and fun could still be had with the cutlery, with the gleam of silver falling through bright air, the delicious thrill of its disappearance into that dangerous foam-laced sapphire. Down went the spoons, into unimaginable depths, where the imagination, none the less, delightedly pursued them. Ships, too, give off a wealth of smells to the dog-like appreciation of early youth. The pitch between the deck planks gave out a tarry tang, engine and kitchen smells floated up the ventilators, the funnels smelt smoky, and the whole ship smelt of being highly cleaned and polished. The passengers smelt of cigarettes and eau-de-Cologne, the Lascars smelt of curry, and the dining saloon smelt of roasting meat and condensed milk. The blue Mediterranean horizon tilted itself slowly across the scuttles, Goanese stewards brought more and more piles of bread and butter. 'No jam on the first slice,' Nanny said. The afternoons went on a long, long time, and the nannies had that time-wasting way of sitting on at the table and talking, generally about infantile ailments, long after the great object, eating, was accomplished. They seemed never to be even mildly intoxicated into violent action by food, as one so invariably was oneself.

Sometimes we went all the way round by sea, plunging down the Channel into the lift of the Atlantic. The Bay of Biscay roared past us and everyone was ill, and the Rock of Gibraltar rose out of the morning mist and was left behind and people started moving their deck-chairs round to the shadier side of the ship. Everyone, not only William and I and Alethea, appeared in white clothes. After tea one played 'Twos and Threes' and 'Puss in the Corner' in the waist of the ship (for ships still had waists in 1913) – 'Don't make them wild, now, May.' Once, ,unforgettably, a four-masted sailing ship under full sail came by in the glow of the late afternoon sun. Every passenger, every child, rushed to the side of the ship, riveted by the romance and beauty of it, as if they knew that such glittering sights would soon no longer be. Sun blazed on the white sails, on the dipping foam-clouded hull, as she cantered on into the Atlantic looking more alive than any ship could be. Often there were dolphins, leaping and playing alongside, and once, with a smell to end smells, an enormous dead whale bumped along the side of the ship. Once a tidal wave broke over the stern of the ship and washed the sewing out of the hands of Louisa, my mother's maid, who was sitting on the deck of the second class making a petticoat. All journeys were made at private expense: there were of course no assisted passages or travel allowances, and families were obliged to spend a considerable portion of their income simply on being together.

There were moments of triumph, moral or athletic. I walked the decks of the *Persia,* so soon to disappear for ever, with my heart swollen with spiritual pride at having, for the first time at the advanced age of three, had my toe-nails cut without crying. I saw everything huge and clear through a blaze of heroism; the painted railings, the scuppers, the colour of the teak deck, the very pattern of the green and white canvas of the deck-chairs. Glorious, glorious, glorious me, I am three, I have had my toenails cut without crying. Several passengers with whom I would not normally have conversed, were put into this sumptuous picture. Every Sunday at sea we sang 'Eternal Father, strong to save' at morning service held in the dining saloon, rearing past mountainous Mediterranean islands or out in the calm blue expanses. The tune had a great swing and was sung with heartfelt enthusiasm by all the congregation. My fifth birthday on board the *Maloja* (also doomed) was hot, calm, and enjoyable. Its centrepieces were a long clothes doll (called Jack from being born at sea) and a square pink cake eaten of rather too freely in a nanny party held in the purser's day cabin. It was a Sunday and I wore my pink sash and did full justice to the hymns. After tea there were sports and I won the flat race and the potato race and an argument about a potato with a boy called Clive Hastings (can he have been?) and life seemed all to be glitter and fulfilment only very slightly tempered by indigestion. After I had gone to bed William, now seven, flown with cake and company, proposed marriage to Eve Westropp, now eight, on the boat deck, and received a qualified assent.

VI

'In the morning Will went in his weird clothes to the opening of the new Legislative Assembly,' my mother recorded in her diary on January 22nd, 1913. 'In P.M. went to see the Tango danced by a Madame Vandyke,' she added. 'Rather pretty as an exhibition but would be impossible in a ballroom.' Legislative Assembly or not, she did not like Will's Egyptian headgear. The wearing of a tarboosh was obligatory on state occasions, but my mother never really cared to see my father in one; perhaps she felt it to be a faint letting down of the crusaders, a joining of the other side, a concession to Islam. My mother did her best to be polite and kind, but it would have been quite impossible for her to form a heartfelt friendship with a Moslem. That terrible centuries-long pincer movement of Islam seems to have been, for Western Europe, one of those traumatic experiences that sink deep into the marrow of the bones. It was a conquest that had so very nearly succeeded that resistance to it was deeply built in; a threat once so real that it could never be forgotten. Christian Europe, although it rarely stopped fighting amongst itself, had feared Islam as a blinding threat to a frail and newly won vision of heaven which seemed to many of them dearer than life itself. Such fears are outside the scope of reason. They thought of Islam as the English and Netherlands Protestants thought of Catholic Spain, as Americans now think of Communist Russia or China (they will probably still be mentally crossing themselves in three hundred years' time). The dread of Islam, because it had lasted for so long, was bred in very deep. It was not only that my mother's forbears had, like most other peoples', clinked and rattled across Europe in their chain armour, sweated in the terrible fevers of Acre, and returned debilitated, unsuccessful, and not much richer, to an arthritic old age in the home counties. The racial memory was reinforced by the stone effigies of crosslegged crusaders in hundreds of village churches and cathedrals up and down England, by pubs called the Saracen's Head, and by the historical novels of Sir Walter Scott, which had been their staple diet in childhood. Like most of her generation my mother saw religious differences in terms of Coeur-de-Lion *v.* Saladin. Spiritually she was still in the pass of Roncesvalles, or battling with paynim hordes at the gates of Vienna and so indeed was I.

By the spring of 1913 I could read enough to keep up in the psalms, which made church even more glamorous and exciting. 'My heart is inditing of a good matter,' I shouted, still off key and slightly behind the music, but wildly enjoying it. The roaring indifferent week-day noise of Moslem Cairo outside in the Boulac Road gave one a superb, onward-Christian-soldiers feeling through which the holiness of Mr Horan and his services made a faint occasional dint. Sitting down, if one moved along the pew one could have a cool piece of wood in the pits of one's knees. When that warmed up, one could move back into one's first place where the wood would have cooled. And then back again.

'Don't fidget, darling.'

So much of childhood is frustrating non-communication. One longs to know how to say, 'I am engaged in a purposeful activity that in no way detracts from my participation in the joys of worship.' How lucky that one cannot; or the resolute self-will of infancy would be even more exhausting to cope with than it is.

My godmother, who happened to be staying at the time, gave me half a sovereign for learning to read properly at four and a half. It would be more to the point if people gave one half a sovereign for not being able to read; reading being in itself a sufficient reward. Life was also simpler in that it was no longer necessary to fox credulous visitors with readings out of the *Child's Garden of Verses*, all of which I knew by heart. The realm of literature was now at my feet, but the half sovereign was instantly taken away from me and put in the bank. Here it would be placed in a small drawer marked Priscilla Hayter, and every so often someone would open the drawer and put in sixpence, thus enabling it to turn into fifteen shillings. I mistrusted this system from the start and I was right. What it actually turned into was about three and sevenpence.

This summer at Compton Manor Alethea was one and a half; could walk, had become conversible. She padded up and down the grassy lane in a broderie anglaise linen hat attended by such of the cousins as were so grievously old that they had come to take an interest in babies. This performance seemed to me to be thought rather too much of by Nanny, and I sloped off under the variegated holly tree and communed sulkily with my lion. At Sidmouth the Atlantic winds rolled in freshly, followed by several weeks of calm. There was a sea-serpent, undulating slowly across the bay, and everyone excitedly pointed it out but I was unable to see what was so special, and was not besides absolutely certain that I was looking in the right direction. The calm brought enormous mackerel shoals. Leaping whitebait, flying before the hungry mackerel shoals, flung themselves upon the beach and could be gathered up live in bucketsful, and pursuing porpoises came close inshore after the mackerel. We seemed always to be hauling in mackerel from our lines, as fast as we could let them out again, and eating them, fried and fresh and delicious. Barrows rolled round Sidmouth in the warm early mornings with the men who wheeled them calling out over and over again, their voices dying away in the distance – 'Mackerel! Fresh Mackerel! Fine Fresh Mack-er-ell!'

An aura of silence and of things unspoken had come to surround the name of Uncle Beachy. Reading letters from Aunt Bay, the other aunts lowered their voices. My grandfather had paid his debts for the seventh and last time and he had been obliged to leave his regiment in circumstances that were kept from us, and to go with Aunt Bay to Canada. Asked about them, the aunts shook their heads in mute sadness. Nothing, however, seemed to depress Aunt Bay, and she reacted with her usual *joie de vivre* to life on the prairies.

My uncle, Arthur Slessor, on the other hand was this summer of 1913 engaged in a correspondence of increasing acrimony with someone called, I think, Mr Schloesser, who, seeing the shape of things to come, had announced in the personal column of *The Times* his intention of taking the name of Slessor. The correspondence began mildly. Would Mr Schloesser mind, my uncle asked, as we were the only family of Slessors in England (they are rife in Aberdeenshire) spelling his new name Slessar, or Slesser? Yes, it appeared, Mr Schloesser would mind. He wanted a real existing name, not a made-up one. He was out for protective colouring, not for originality. The correspondence thereafter degenerated. I hope that the word Jew was not used in a pejorative sense; I feel certain that the word German was. Mr Schloesser eventually won this conflict, game, set, and match, by declaring in a superb burst of spirit fully appreciated by my uncle, that he would not only spell his name Slessor, but that he and his sons henceforth and for ever would, if asked, or even if not asked, declare themselves to be first cousins of my uncle and his brother. This hatchet was finally buried in 1950, after Slessors of both Scots and German origin had got themselves killed in several wars, when John Henry's grandson, Brigadier Harry Slessor (brave, affectionate and mild, an ornament to his profession), asked Mr Philip Slessor of the B.B.C., son of Mr Schloesser, to lunch, where they regaled each other with excerpts from the correspondence. It had, however, one side effect which would have charmed my uncle, had he known of it. Later in the year a highly intelligent young lawyer called Henry Schloesser, afterwards Attorney General in the first Labour Government, when de-Germanizing his name, nervously spelt it Slesser.

Life in Egypt this winter, barring a few stormy interludes, was fine and calm. I could read, and turn back somersaults. The rabbits, always previously thought to be both boys, had cleverly given birth to five charming young. I could swing very high, and play 'Old Maid' and 'Beggar my Neighbour' without having to be told which were Kings and which were Knaves. William, with commendable patience, was teaching me draughts, and backgammon, though I never looked like shaping up into a worthy opponent. Most wonderful of all, my clothes had sometimes stopped being white, or at least all-white. The darkest thoughts that cross the minds of little girls are in connection with the apparel imposed upon them by their elders. How boring they were, those white clothes! How insufferably tame and smug and separate and unnecessary, imposing as they seemed to do, an everlasting obligation to be good. Plain white muslin always, unless it were embroidered, or plain white wool. Sundays and high days were made resplendent for me by the tying on of the pink sash. Bursting with vainglory, I stood before the long looking-glass in my parents' bedroom, contemplating my reflection with undiluted enthusiasm. 'Handsome is', Nanny predictably said, 'as handsome does.' The moment of wearing for the first time a white linen dress embroidered beautifully in red by my mother was a moment of ecstasy. Still more wonderful, I soon afterwards had a blue linen dress embroidered in white. Alethea, poor two-year-old, was still confined to tedious white muslin. I walked under the leboc avenues in a transcendent glow of sophistication, blue-clad, scuffing the dust into my sandals and out again, a Queen of Sheba before the brush with Solomon, heedless of reproof or admonition. I am blue, I am blue, in a blue linen dress, I am five, I am blue, I am five. This paean of vainglory absorbed my being. I am Me, in a blue linen dress, WITH BLUE LINEN KNICKERS TO MATCH.

Sometimes my heart stopped inditing of a good matter and I experienced a sharp return into infancy. I got out of bed one evening with a pain that dulled my mind and quickened all my senses.

'Where's Mother and Father?'

'Gone to dinner with some Egyptians,' Nanny said, disapprovingly, 'as well you know seeing that I heard the mistress telling you.'

'I want them. I *want* them.'

'Then want must be your master, seeing that it's past eight at night, and they have said good night and gone . . . Why what are you doing getting in my lap, and you a great girl of five?'

The pain was too dull, too insistent. I could think of no name for it.

'Tears now. What next? It's as well William sleeps in the master's dressing-room now. What would he say, to see you crying with no reason given?'

Suddenly, with relief, I remembered the name for it.

'I've got a year-ache.'

A total change of front. Sympathy, remedies, warm oil, rocking. And the only palliative there is for infant grief, the concentrated attention of a familiar and loving human being.

'Sing, Nanny, sing.' One could turn again to the comfort of tyranny, without fear of being rebuked for being a baby, could insist, mercilessly, upon the distraction of being carried by sound and movement into a different world where one's ear ache would be unable to pursue.

'Sing, Nanny.'

She went through her repertoire. Bent over me, she rocked me with the timeless rhythmic patience of women with an ailing child. The others were asleep and forgotten. She was all mine.

'Sing "Now the day is over". Sing, Nanny. Go on.'

> 'Now the day is over
> Night is drawing nigh,
> Shadows of the evening
> Steal across the sky.'

Steal. They stole across the sky, so of course they were robbers. The leader of the shadows had the face of Barabbas. They rode black horses across the sunset, over the wide expanse of sky from Rhoda Island to Em-baba. They were hooded, swarthy Mamelouke figures, crowding out the light.

'Sing, Nanny. Go on.' She went on. Slowly, imperceptibly, the pain spread out from me to her, spread wider, further, became an echo of itself. 'Sing it again.'

'Now the darkness gathers
Stars begin to peep,
Birds and beasts and flowers
Soon will be asleep.'

The bright blue of the morning glories shrivelled into their afternoon mauveness, the hibiscus shut up their red gramophone trumpets with dusk.

'Jesu, give the weary
Calm and sweet repose;'

Especially the donkeys and the camels, folding up their tired legs in the dust.

'Go on, Nanny. Why are you stopping in the middle?'

'Grant to little children
Visions bright of Thee;
Guard the sailors tossing
On the deep blue sea.'

Hundreds of little walnut-shell boats, matchstick-masted, rushed up gentian coloured walls of Mediterranean waves, were juggled in the foam, came down again. Why worry about the sailors tossing on the deep blue sea? They were all having enormous fun anyway.

'Comfort every sufferer
Watching late in pain'

Under the arched roofs of mud-walled Egyptian houses,

dimly-lit, an endless succession of Jairus's daughters were laid out on the bare floors. Men at the pool of Bethesda were stretched on pallets; long-robed, helpless, gasping in the close air. The sickening, pungent, full-bodied smell of Egypt came out at one like the kick of a mule.

> 'Those who plan some evil
> From their sin restrain.'

Gathered in the linen-room, under a naked light, Ali-Baba and as many of the forty thieves as could crowd in, laid their heads together, nodding and villainous under their burnouses. Below the crowded stars Judas went stealthily out into the cricket-shrilling night.

'Go on, Nanny. Why are you stopping?'

> 'When the morning wakens
> Then may I arise,
> Pure and fresh and sinless
> In Thy holy eyes.'

Clean socks, and all that; but will that morning ever come?
'Sing it again, Nanny. Sing it. Sing it again.'
Patiently, Nanny cleared her throat and began again.
May came to the door and was nodded away. At intervals, she reappeared. Nanny's supper grew cold on the sewing-room table. Her tea stewed in its pot.

> 'And to Thee, Blest Spirit
> Whilst all ages run.'

The pain had long since vanished, but I was awake enough not to tell her this. It had left me with a weary hollowness, an aching blank that wanted neither food nor drink nor warm oil in the ear, but which desperately needed company, that feared to be left alone with nothing but itself. For half an hour, for an hour, for an eternity, she and I had been one flesh, a communal being. In pain and in solace we had dissolved into each other. A near-mother, she had taken me back into her womb. In the darkness and the stillness I feared the harsh necessity of being re-born. She must stay with me now until I slept. This too she fully understood, and sat unmoving while very reluctantly and with bumpings and jerkings and shudderings into wakefulness I went gradually to sleep.

VII

The fateful summer of 1914 found us as tenants of Radway
Manor, a furnished house at Sidmouth; Alethea and I promoted to the progressive splendour of being allowed to wear
dark blue shorts and jerseys on the beach like our brother and
cousins. This daring innovation disconcerted some of the
older Cousin Neils almost more than the outbreak of hostilities, which was, after all, no new thing. Their melancholy,
already profound, seemed perceptibly to deepen over the
shorts. They read each other out long letters in spidery hand-
writing on black-edged writing paper – 'Jess tells me that the
greenfly on the roses has never been so bad, and poor
Bernard's lumbago is no better.'

Sidmouth, as a place full of people as distinct from one surrounded with high red cliffs, was slowly coming into focus.
All about, and more thickly at the other end of the town,
dwelt another species of human being, who were called poor
people. Always to be treated with kindness, like chronic
invalids; to be given one's spare pocket-money, extra toys,
out-grown clothes, scamped prayers; they were a milling
world of separated beings whose lot could be mitigated but
never altered. Think, the grown-ups constantly adjured us,
and not only *à propos* of the unfinished food on our plates, of

the poor people. Basically splendid, and members of the club, because also English; wearing ill-fitting boots and stiff collars, alarmed and conventional and always to be jollied along, they had string hair and slightly mocking faces, and existed in a world of their own in which they appeared not unhappy. They had a sort of resilience and cohesion, an occasional doughty all-in-the-same-boat defiance, an unsquashable barefoot cockiness that invited respect. From time to time one got the message that they did not particularly *want* one to be kind. In the country things felt rather different, perhaps because everyone had gardens where they grew vegetables and kept hens and sometimes a pig, and because there were more jobs. No one seemed so specifically rich or poor or separate, they simply did different kinds of work. Uncles, gardeners, cowmen, parsons, farmers and grooms seemed much the same; getting on with their lives and addressing each other without deference or patronage.

The poor of England were a sort of relief after the poor of Egypt. Demonstrably wretched, abject, and begging, these came into an altogether alien and rather shuddery category. Thronging together with a kind of headstrong mutual indifference, poor people in Egypt treated each other ill, preyed upon each other, took swift and unscrupulous advantage of each other's least weaknesses, like flies quarrelling round jam. Seen through the orgulous grey eyes of the west, they appeared to debase the currency of humanity. Their snatching hands were formed, horribly, in the same mould as one's own. What went home with an occasional appalled pang, was that it was among just such people that Christ had lived his life. They made the whole idea of Christianity impossibly difficult, and I was very cross indeed with them about that, for who could love such neighbours as these? Possible perhaps to take a deep breath and love Lady Brunyate, but could anyone love Egyptian beggars? Their lot was terrifyingly parlous. 'Poor things, they're only heathens,' Nanny said, 'what can you expect?' and even William, a tiger for accuracy, had given up telling her that this was not so. The scorching poverty of the east was insoluble and gave one's heart a restlessness and a discomfort from which it was a relief to get back to the scrubbed defiant English.

I was now sufficiently confident of my parents to enjoy their laughter, to take a delight in laughing with them at what was only intermittently comprehensible. I slept one night in a camp bed at the foot of theirs and woke up to hear them having an amiable argument about whether my father had or had not snored. 'Father's snoring', I said, clinching the argument, 'was like the roaring of a hundred thousand lions.' My parents thought this funny; their laughter made a warm rich noise. Carried away by my wit and charm, I showed off at breakfast, spilt my milk, and was told by Nanny to sit square and stop acting simple. Someone had sprinkled the raspberries with salt instead of castor sugar, and the nannies made this ridiculous excuse for not letting us eat them. The day, which was July the 27th, got better as it wore on. The afternoon tide was low, a plenitude of red wet sand appeared. We sat on rugs by the sea wall, in a covey of starchy nannies, eating an endless series of lightly sanded honey sandwiches, unaware that the Archduke Franz Ferdinand of Austria had been shot just a month ago in the streets of Sarajevo.

The coming of the 1914 world war coincided with the arrival of the circus and seemed to me very jolly indeed with the bands and the singing of patriotic songs and the elephants and the sea-lions and the hue and cry after German spies. 'If we keep a good look out on the wall we are pretty sure to catch one,' William assured us, and there we sat, figures of settled determination, scrutinizing every passer-by for signs of a cloven hoof. How are we to tell them, I thought, but was not mug enough to ask. Uncles and fathers went away, of course, but then they were always going, it was part of the pattern of life. The splendours of the sea and beach were there as usual, even if things were a trifle up-ended. There were always the wineberries and the apricots in the walled kitchen garden, the hay in the loft, the two ponies in the orchard. Only Aunt Meg cast a note of gloom. 'Tinker, Tailor, Soldier, Sailor, Gentleman, Apothecary, Ploughboy, Thief' we chanted over our fruit-salad stones (lunch downstairs on Sunday). 'Tinker, Tailor, Soldier – I'm going to marry a soldier!' 'Don't, children, don't,' Aunt Meg would cry, putting up her hands to cover her ears. Were things, perhaps, not quite as they had been? Was there a gloom, a shadow, over the Edwardian summer of our parents' lives? Nanny was reading William and me *The Gorilla Hunters;* the two dark bay ponies in the orchard seemed suddenly to look like two lurking gorillas, to rush at one, to necessitate a rapid leap into the hazel tree. On the stairs was a picture of the Devil tempting Saint Anthony, which exercised a strong horror-fascination; whether to rush past it with averted gaze, whether to linger by it and look closely at it and drink deeply of its dreadfulness? Perhaps if one swallowed it whole it couldn't frighten one again. One evening May dressed up as a ghost and floated suddenly out of the barn, frightening Alethea into tears and being severely reprimanded by Nanny. Grown-ups scolding grown-ups, how unsure are the foundations of the world! Next day Alethea roamed about with a storm-washed expression, pushing a small wooden wheelbarrow with a hole in it, out of which her doll, Affa-Caffa, fell with monotonous regularity and was given in her turn a severe scolding. Other nannies were heard to make comments about people getting out of bed on the wrong side. Even Alethea, though but two, had been made aware of something cataclysmic in the air when my father left so abruptly as not to be able to accompany her on a farewell visit to the little pigs. It is a bleak moment when people one loves inexplicably fail to reciprocate by taking a passionate interest in one's enthusiasms. What was war, that it could deflect people from little pigs? Affa-Caffa fell once more from the wheelbarrow and was sharply bitten for her negligence by Alethea. Sawdust streamed from Affa-Caffa's punctured frame, causing wild tears of remorse and guilt from Alethea, and alarm and despondency from all those spectators who were not small boys, to whom a doll-disaster or two rarely comes amiss. In the walled garden the wineberries fell squashily, the loganberries seemed to stay permanently unripe.

The Victoria plums were beset by wasps, preventing them from being beset by us. Hamer was badly stung and his face swelled up and it seemed to cause less stir than usual. A sultry August feeling hung about. Surely the grown-ups were less concentrated upon their only really important task, us?

By October William and I were taking the war seriously. It had come to stay, and we joined in the knitting of an enormous khaki scarf. There was a children's play in which I was cajoled into taking a soppy part called the Fairy Dewdrop, wearing pale green net and a heavy scowl. Mutinous three-year-olds dressed as elves skipped sullenly round the clock golf course. '*So* pretty,' the aunts said, and some unlucky Belgian refugees were swept in to be taken out of themselves by watching it. Alethea, in red sateen, sensibly stayed in the shrubbery when the moment for her entrance came, and I was left with my wand, sourly repeating her cue. The hapless Belgians with nowhere else to go were obliged to sit through it in silent contempt and must have heartily wished themselves back amongst the Uhlans undergoing less refined forms of outrage.

War, as the days drew in, became ever more gloomy. There was difficulty in getting passages to Egypt; what is more surprising is that they were available at all. The lease of Radway ended, we moved into rooms at Fortfield Terrace which looked across the cricket field to the sad November sea. Lights had to be dowsed at night for fear of German submarines which were said to be lurking offshore and only waiting the least gleam in order to bombard us. The agonies endured by the few whose shoulders held the skies suspended communicated themselves dimly to us through the expressions upon grown-up faces. We had never before seen the trees blown bare by winter winds, and accustomed ourselves in a bewildered way to this English season, to the long melancholy of late autumn dusks. 'Edward', the grown-ups said to each other, 'is missing.' Missing what? 'And Rupert, in the Hogue.' Cousin Bob, commanding the 4th Guards Brigade in the retreat from Mons, emerged alive but terribly wounded, 'Teeny tells me that his right leg will never'. . . Their voices dropped. His right leg will never what? Faces seemed shocked, long, unlaughing; the weather of infancy had broken for good, and the wind blew cold and steady off the grey sea.

We left England in December, crossing by night from Southampton to le Havre; there was to be no more going 'long sea' by Gibraltar. The weather seemed in keeping with the world event. The P. & O. express hurled itself across France through a wild evening of storm; French soldiers were huddled against the wind on every platform. There was thunder, lightning, and gale, through which Nanny could be seen implacably making tea and boiling our milk on the spirit lamp in the tea basket as the train rocked and roared down the long central plains of France. Something must have gone wrong, unaccountably we spent the rest of the night in a hotel in Lyons, while the front part of the train, with cots and baggage, sped on to Marseilles. In the hotel bedroom Nanny doggedly scrubbed out the bottom drawer of the chest of drawers (the deepest one) for Alethea to sleep in. All was irregular and confusing and we had not had enough sleep to enjoy it. Next morning I left my lion behind in the hotel dining-room, a kind head-waiter came running down the platform with him just as the train was starting.

'Lyons,' Nanny said, as the signal box flicked past, 'funny place to go leaving your lion in.'

'He must have wanted', May said irrepressibly, 'to stay and play with all the other lions.'

'Sst!' Nanny warned. She could never be sure that May would not go putting ideas into heads that had far too many already, let alone being overdone with travelling. She opened her special Gladstone-shaped leather handbag and took out a duster. No child of hers was allowed to take off its gloves in a railway carriage until the whole place had been properly cleaned. You never knew. The handbag, kept locked against all the predatory Egyptians, all the unreliable continentals, contained also a sponge and towel, Scotts Emulsion, Syrup of Figs, pommade divine for bruises, and Brand's essence of beef for those recovering from seasickness and stomach upsets. There were also, supplied by the Army and Navy Stores, packets of paper covers for lavatory seats, so that our little bottoms should not rest where those suspect continental bottoms so recently had rested. You never knew.

In the Hotel Terminus at Marseilles two Frenchmen with napkins tied round their necks were eating delicious-looking ham off blue plates, surrounded by a twirl of cress. I requested a like diet.

'Cress' Nanny said. 'In *France*! The very idea!'

The P. & O. liner, lysolled within an inch of its life, swept us from these unsalutary shores.

It was always wonderful to arrive, but never more so than now, just before Christmas. On the platform of Cairo station was my father, large and reassuring behind his lion-coloured moustache, and accompanied by Mohammed and Ismaïn wearing overcoats over their galabiehs. The horses' hooves clanged across the iron of the Boulac bridge, the lights of Kasr-el-Nil spilled in long streamers, the familiar Nile rolled darkly under. Em-baba trams swung past, full of the same gleaming forty-thief faces. In the house it was still, there was a blessed silence, an un-movingness. The world had once more ceased to rock and roll. There were the same H.P. biscuits for nursery supper, the same Egyptian milk, so much thinner and less creamy than the English kind, so flat and boiled and right. There was the same red patterned stool by which one knelt to say Our Father. Outside in the stillness and darkness the cicadas shrieked their familiar lullaby. Other people, grown-ups, talked about England as home, but we knew better. This, for richer or poorer, was it – with the red stair carpet and the wide cool hall reaching up to the roof, and the faintly clinical dust of the eucalyptus blossom blowing in over the window-sills.

VIII

My mother and her sisters were true Victorians; not in a general way frightened of battle, murder, and sudden death, but perfectly terrified of insects. Opening her first Egyptian orange to find it full of life, she had been unable to eat another orange for several years. There had been a shattering moment on her first day in our newly built house in Zamalek, when a praying mantis alighted in her open cabin trunk. With a wild cry she shut the lid and locked the trunk and piled it high with heavy dictionaries until my father's return from work. A mole-cricket was a thing she could not bring herself to think about. She never lost her horror of the large Egyptian black beetles in the garden, nor for that matter did I, and could always be routed by William brandishing one. The discovery of a scorpion in the nursery toy cupboard was, I think, kept from her.

'Come and look, Nanny, what there is! A tiny little lobster in one of the dolls' tea cups.'

There it sat, registering apparent good will, and caused a furore. Mohammed and Ahmed were summoned; and even they looked serious and alarmed and repeatedly shook out their long galabiehs during the hunt. Once, thrillingly, there was a cobra at the grotto, and earlier still, on a picnic to the pyramids, May had been found by Nanny to be playing with a scorpion, poking it idly with a small stick, totally unaware of its potency. She was forcibly impressed with the narrowness of this escape.

'Within three inches of death,' she kept saying to Nanny at nursery breakfast next morning, 'I was within *three inches* of death.'

'Oh well,' Nanny said comfortably, 'I daresay we've all had narrower escapes than we know.' She poured May out another cup of tea. The sun streamed in through the open fly-netted sewing-room window. 'Elbows off the table, William Bad-enough,' for William's second name, which was Goodenough, was a source of endless nursery wit.

All the same, it was an impressive thought, and I was impressed too, although death at this time held no terrors. All was clearly arranged in my mind. When the summons came I would carefully climb up an endless long ladder stretching high into the brilliance of the blue Egyptian sky. Far below, the goats, poor fellows, would all be streaming off disappoint-edly over the Zamalek bridge in the general direction of Em-baba. The judgment seat of God was, inexplicably, sited at the tram stop on the near side of the bridge. Emphatically numbered amongst the sheep, I would be wearing my best lace petticoat, a flannel petticoat with scalloped edges, and a pair of best knickers with pink ribbon threaded through them. Closely behind me would follow May, clad in her Sunday dark blue skirt and white blouse, carrying my best dress and pink sash over one arm. (No one in their senses climbs ladders wearing their best dress.) On a sort of crystal railway platform at the top we should pause, while May put on my dress and tied my sash. Here a slight doubt rose, the perennial question of whether or not one wears a hat. Could Heaven be classified as church or home? What May did after discharging her essential function was also a little uncertain, but she probably faded into the middle distance where she would for ever remain, peacefully turning down celestial night-nursery beds.

My own course was perfectly clear. Saint Peter (and what has he done to deserve an eternity of conciergehood?) would fling back the gates and I would be received, amidst universal enthusiasm, into the presence of God. It would be like going down into the drawing-room in the evenings, only more so. One would have a fascinating time getting to know all those extremely farouche characters in the Bible, and I had also always wanted to get in among all those little galabiehed figures around the knees of Christ and teach them a thing or two, such as hide-and-seek and blowing their noses, which, judging by their present-day prototypes visible around the streets of Cairo and Gezira, they simply did not know.

There was indeed, nothing *to* death; and the Holy Ghost was a character I particularly wanted to get to know better. In the teeth of all the available information, I believed him to be a boy of about fifteen, with wings like a swan and the ability to be in a great many different places at once. Tirelessly on the wing, and with his cheeks for ever bulged out in the manner of the winds in old maps, he blew courage, truthfulness, and a disposition to fold up their underclothes into people's hearts, like a character permanently inflating balloons for a party. I had once called on him, when entirely surrounded by wolves in bed at night. I had counted at least eleven of them, and several more could be clearly heard scratching and snuffling under the bed. The only thing that stopped them from springing was their fear of getting their feet tangled in the mosquito net, but you could feel their hunger gaining on them. The Holy Ghost had responded smartly by sending me to sleep, and in the morning the wolves, as is their wont, had sloped off. Taking things all round, the company would, on the whole, be better in heaven. A few of them, of course, would not be English, but they would all (except for Jesus who even then was recognisably in a different category) be in process of learning, gently but firmly, how to be.

Shortly after her brush with the scorpion, May escaped her heavenly destiny by leaving to get married. She was, she told us, going to have a boy and a girl, called Armand and Antoinette. The war swept her from us, and we never heard whether this plan was carried out. She was replaced by Ena, rather more fubsy and kind, and extremely songful.

'Daisy, Daisy, give me your answer, do!' Ena would sing as she looped up the mosquito nets and made the beds. But what *was* her aunt's ado? This was another of the many questions it was too late to ask, for fear of risking that superior grown-up laughter. 'Eat up your porridge, William, without more ado,' Nanny often said; but could anybody really want Daisy's aunt's fuss? Perhaps all childhoods are much alike, but no one can have lived in a more steady haze of verbal confusion than

I did. 'When the golden sun sinks in the west', Ena went on, 'and the toil of the long day is o'er.' Her voice rose into a prolonged and jolly wail. In fact it is difficult to imagine what toil she and Nanny can have done all the long day. Certainly the Berberine servants were never allowed to boil the nursery milk or make the nursery beds. Suliman was graciously permitted to scrub and sweep the nursery floors, and Mohammed must have been allowed in my father's dressing-room to put out his clothes. My father in any case came into a different category and was not haunted by fears of germs or unwashed hands and seemed increasingly to regard Egyptians simply as other men, generally in need of jobs, food, shelter, and good government. Perhaps Nanny and Ena, in between long cheerful sessions after meals when they told each other's fortunes in tea-leaves, ceaselessly washed and ironed the white clothes we all always wore; or made more of them, floppy starched linen hats, embroidered nightgown yokes, scalloped edged flannel petticoats, lace-insertion knickers; and ironed for William what must have been an endless supply of white shorts.

This was the winter of the locusts, the winter of the Australians; difficult to say which arrival was more exciting. The locusts came first, appearing in an arrowhead of glittering diamonds against the azure brightness of the sky, against the noonday blaze of the sun. Soon the air was thick with them, a million darting splinters of red glass. What was worse was that they were beginning to settle. An atavistic panic fury seized on the entire household. My parents were out, and Nanny was looking after Alethea, but everyone else stopped doing everything and set about the locusts; capturing, stamping, netting, banging, and knocking them out with brooms. The cook stopped cooking and Ena stopped ironing. William tore about with his butterfly net, enraptured by this rich and solid prey. Ismaïn was in the forefront, his helpers raged furiously to and fro. Even Mohammed lost his massive calm, his grave upper-Nile dignity. Ahmed and Suliman and the marmitone were beings possessed. They ran about the newly dug and dusty field between us and the bridge, with their galabiehs flying wildly. Their arms flailed; sweat streamed from the bronze foreheads under their tarbooshes; they uttered wild Nilotic pre-Arabic cries. By their frenzy we were given to understand that it would be our survival or that of the locusts. Sanction was thus given to that unslaked passion for inflicting death that lurks in more human hearts than would like to think it did. Slaughter on a great scale was accomplished amidst cries of rapture and yells of hate and triumph. Provided with a small string tennis racket, I laid about me with a right good will. Whang, bang, whoosh! All was dust, heat, effort; all was whizzing and whirling and buzzing; all was unity and clamour and a great sighing release of aggression as we battled against this seemingly unstoppable foe. Onward Christian soldiers, whang, whoosh, bang! When the swarm had passed and the gardens were more or less saved and this jolly orgy was over, Nanny could be seen, unruffled in her starched apron, drying William's wild black hair with a bath towel, a reproving and civilized expression on her face.

'Time for rest, Priscilla dear.'

Rest. Hated, hateful word. 'Look at your pinafore, too. You'd better put her right in the bath, Ena.'

'Can't I look at a book?'

'No book today; you didn't finish your egg at breakfast.'

Hated rest. Nothing to do but twist the folds of the mosquito net between one's toes. Hateful boring rest. The carving on the top of the wardrobe looked like two open-mouthed sharks converging on a small round boy. Could he ever get away? Must the sharks get him?

'Can't I look at a book *now*?'

'No, dear. I've told you. Rest flat on your back. It's time to rest.'

'I am sorry, Nanny,' I said, years later, it seemed, 'but if Heaven is Eternal Rest, I am not going there.'

'And that's no way to talk, either.'

Religion was dangerous ground with Nanny. One could not, as with one's parents, say anything, any time. Nanny's lips had a way of folding up, forbiddingly. The first time I heard the word Alleluia I was so enchanted with it that I spent ten minutes leaping up and down on the armchair in the far corner of the drawing-room loudly pronouncing it.

'Don't do that,' Nanny said, when she found me. Her voice had an edge.

'Alleluia!' I said, leaping higher. The springs sent one up and up, the sensation was glorious. Alleluia! Alleluia! Alleluia! It was highly enjoyable; I wanted never to stop.

'I said don't do that,' Nanny said again, more sharply. 'You'll break the springs.' But one could tell it wasn't that she minded. 'Alleluia! Alleluia!' I said, boring of it very slightly but drawing her on. 'All-el-uia-a-a!'

'That's a holy word,' Nanny said, 'not to be bandied about in play. I would think you'd know better.' She took me by the arm quite brusquely and led me off to have my face washed although we both knew that it was perfectly clean.

The arrival of the Australians was scarcely less dramatic and their stay lasted longer. Suddenly Egypt was full of sunburned cockney strangers, with glinting eyes and a total disregard of authority. They wore large felt hats, turned up at one side. They looked like cavalier hats without the ostrich feather – 'When did you last see your father?' But the Australians had clearly never seen their fathers, mothers, or Nannies. They were blissfully naughty boys for ever out on some gigantic spree. They raced each other up and down the Great Pyramid; within the first fortnight ten of them broke their necks falling down it. It was put out of bounds, and they gave a repeat performance up King Zoser's Step Pyramid at Sakhara. They sat all over the tops of the trams, even the trams from wicked Em-Baba full of forty thieves; great laughing sprawls of Australians, disregarding the Egyptian tram-conductors, shouting, smoking, laughing, singing, and constantly getting themselves electrocuted. They raced each other along the parapets of the Nile bridges for bets and fell off into the river and were drowned. They did everything that no one else was allowed to do. In its uncounted years of history Egypt had probably never seen anything quite like them before; cockney wit and hardihood warmed up to boiling point by a hundred years of good food and hot sun. Many had been before who would risk their lives for a belief or a dream or for spoils, but none who would throw away their lives so entirely for the fun of it. Ena and I fell in love with the entire Australian army, and this feeling was clinched by a Brisbane sergeant who gave William and me a boomerang, probably in order to get us to go away and throw it while he talked to Nanny, who seemed to us as old as the Sphinx but was actually a fair, freckled, and attractive thirty-three.

William and I both tried to throw the boomerang together, it went from us unexpectedly, sailed across the road and lodged in a tree, a golden mohr in the garden of the house opposite, and I took a deep breath and gathered myself to yell.

'Who lives there?' the sergeant asked. 'One of them pashas?'

'Sir Ronald and Lady Sybil Graham,' Nanny told him, Nannyishly.

'Sweet Fanny Adams and all,' the sergeant said, Australianly, 'it's all one to me.' He was across the road and through the Grahams' gate and up the tree and back with the boomerang almost before I had time to put my yell back where it came from.

'Without so much as a by your leave or a with your leave,' Nanny pointed out to him, 'or ringing of the doorbell either. Of all the cheek – ' It was news that grown-ups too, could show cheek, and that other grown-ups could, however reprovingly, be pleased about it.

It seemed as if nothing could stop the Australians. But they were stopped for ever, all too many of them, at Gallipoli, for which destination they presently left. So also were two charming New Zealander cousins, who came to stay with us on their way to the Dardanelles, Leslie Hore and Cyril Hayter, quiet spare figures, very well-held and purposeful, who had left their faraway farms where everything depended upon them, to cross the long slow oceans and die in a European quarrel which they deeply felt to be also their own. This breath of heroism, aloof or lively, hung expectantly on the air of Cairo, before they all went away to leave their bones on the saddest promontory in the world, Gallipoli; the promontory where the war might have ended two years earlier than it did, the promontory where allied victory might have saved Russia from communism and Germany from nazism; the place of twenty million ghosts, the promontory where the second world war might have avoided ever being fought.

An uncle, passing through Egypt on his way from India to the fighting in France, gave William his first knife, with which he instantly repaired to the garden and cut a gash in one of the leather joints which held together the galvanised iron sections of the hose. A merry fountain ensued, in which William was ecstatically drenched to the skin. This enjoyable experience was unaccountably considered by the grown-ups to be a sufficient punishment for his action, and scarcely the ghost of a scolding followed the event. The simplicity of adults is sometimes amazing. Surely they must know that being soused to the skin in all one's clothes is one of life's keenest pleasures?

Next morning, accused at breakfast of riotous behaviour likely to cause a breach of the peace, William was sent away from table to finish his bacon in the chill solitude of the linen room. The ominous phrase, 'Time for his prep-school', began to be heard on people's lips, but what did they mean? School, as everyone knew, was Miss Quibell's. 'Elbows off the table, dear,' Nanny said, 'and say your grace *clearly*. Don't let me hear you mumble it, the way you sometimes do, with your mind here, there and everywhere.'

Nineteen-fifteen had a falling away feeling about it. This, sadly, was now revealed to be the last winter of William's company. He was to go to his prep-school in the spring, and be left behind in England when we came back to Egypt in the autumn. No one had consulted me about this arrangement, and I deplored it. Small children seem able to love and resent each other, to miss each other and to be indifferent to each other, all at the same time. I had been terrified by him over the black beetle threats, and grateful to him over baths, in which, owing to my persistent fear of being the baby who went out with the bath water, he always gallantly took the tap end. I had been jealous of William for being older, for being a boy, for being so much more highly regarded by Mohammed and Abdu and Ahmed and all, for being the centrepiece, for being the right sex in a man's country. He had been jealous of me for my dexterous and deceitful way of getting out of trouble, which he scorned to emulate; for trying to be a pseudo boy and then rapidly switching back into being a little girl when it seemed more politic to trade on the curls and muslin aspect. We had had endless fun. We had enjoyed together those sumptuous and pointless hullaballoos of cheerful din that are so much more satisfactory made by two people than by only one, all those thunderings up and down landings for the sake of thunder, all those shoutings and yellings for the pure joy of noise. We had fought often enough. We used to rage and stamp and yell and tear each other's hair out. As his was perfectly black, and mine very fair, there was never any doubt about whose hands had been at work. Once, in a blood row in the potting shed, I had taken a trowel and scratched his brand new trolley all down its painted side, in revenge for his scorn of my doll's pram, and he had seized up a garden fork and thrown it at me, missing my eye by a fraction of an inch, and leaving a neat little lifelong scar on my temple. This was money for old rope. Shining with innocence and streaming with the most satisfactory amount of blood, I had rushed shrieking into the house; making ample capital out of an incident for which I was almost wholly to blame; becoming every instant more tiny, martyred, and female. Perhaps everything in our early life has its point, and sharing a nursery with me steeled William in later years against throwing garden forks at Messrs Bulganin and Khrushchev.

Goodbye now to all those trains and stations, all those zouaves and hussars and lancers, forts and cruisers and guns that had so boringly occupied the nursery floor. More living space, now, for dolls and dolls' tea-parties. Yet nursery life seemed flat and dull without him, and Alethea was only three.

He knew, even at eight and a half, so many of the answers, and was rarely a bully. I missed him very much, and very much enjoyed having things more my own way. What are games of house without a father? But then there was the freedom to use his trolley. I adapted; and grew steadily more tiresome without him.

IX

The P. & O. liner, black and buff and not yet camouflaged, swung out of Port Said roads. The low land dwindled into a line, into a nothing; we zig-zagged steadily through the Mediterranean once again, with William's no longer wanted sun helmet trailing on a long string astern. Foam lay far behind us across the calm blue sea in a series of long or short limbed zeds. Things are never fully explained to children, or perhaps one never listens to the last half of an explanation because one's mind is so busy absorbing the first half. I knew that there were German submarines waiting to torpedo our ship, but not that we zig-zagged on an irregular course in order to make their aim more difficult. I knew that the Germans had laid mines in order that allied ships should strike them and sink, but not that these lay in small and localized minefields. I imagined the whole ocean thick with mines like marbles scattered across the nursery floor. In which case it would have been more logical, as well as quicker and braver, to have gone straight through, instead of all this hapless jinking about. Why did nobody tell the captain? Why didn't William? Why didn't Nanny, come to that? I wondered whether to undertake the task myself. But what would be the good? Grown-ups are so often hopelessly illogical and self-willed.

Colonialism was at this time dawning in my mind, although as yet I lacked the nerve to colonize the captain of a liner. Armed with habeas corpus and a tin of Keatings, I would have colonized with the furthest flung and best. I shared to the full in that well known Anglo-Saxon vice of wanting to put things right, and believing that with a little brisk common sense, this can be achieved once and for all. This it was which caused us, in a wave of enthusiasm, to acquire a vast empire in order to prevent its inhabitants from carving each other up, allowing their babies to die of dirt, and tormenting their over-loaded beasts of burden, and which equally caused us, some hundreds of years later, to give it all up long before these laudable objects had been accomplished.

I left the captain to his own devices, not really minding at this time whether we were torpedoed or not. I was very uncertain about what an explosion was, but I knew about shipwreck and liked what I knew. One stepped into a lifeboat, and after an agreeable interval passed in eating dog-biscuits and drinking water out of tin soap-dishes, grounded on the nearest island and spent several pleasurable days living in a shelter of boughs and taming turtles; a programme which nobody could despise. The Mediterranean was full of sparsely inhabited islands calling out for just such an event. They floated tantalisingly past in the warm spring sunshine, but it was a bore having to have the portholes tightly shut all the time. Why? Because, William explained with unwonted patience, if we were torpedoed the sea would rush in at too many places and we should quickly sink before we could get into the boats. But it was all unreal, had but an academic interest.

We arrived safely in England, and William, pale but resolute in a new suit and a stiff collar, set forth for Copthorne, a prep-school run by the brother of Monty Rendall, then headmaster of Winchester. The mists of school swirled over his head, he was lost to us, existed only in short stilted letters that sounded like someone else. On her way back in the train my mother, already miserable at parting from him, was further depressed to read in the evening papers of the sinking of the *Lusitania*. This shocking news, involving great loss of life, did not deter her from our planned return to Egypt by sea in the autumn.

The Slessor sisters, drawn ever closer by the miseries of war, converged again in a furnished house at Sidmouth. Meadhurst was nearer to the sea than Radway, but not a proper house with fields and stables and walled gardens. It had laburnums and a glassed verandah, and not nearly such a plenitude of dark shrubbery and green lawn. Our buckets and spades and ribbons of drying seaweed lived out their lives in a tiled porch under the glow of stained yellow and red glass. This summer, without William, we came under the undisputed sway of Hamer, now a doughty seven-year-old with a complete absence of physical fear and a general scorn of nannydom. His mother was having another baby and his father was fighting in France; he had time on his hands in which to form us into a small but compact expeditionary force. Under his auspices we enjoyed the great and glorious day of running away. Alethea, a three-year-old in broderie anglaise petticoats and not really dressed for campaigning, was lured from the nursery and hauled, alarmed but game, over a series of stone walls and through innumerable thorn hedges. All day long we hid and skirmished, ranging the little western valley stream, munching buns, lying hidden in other people's gardens, climbing their trees, rifling their birds' nests, stealing unripe gooseberries, intoxicated with our cleverness and daring. Whenever invention failed or interest flagged, Peggy Barnard was quick to think up a fresh notion, a new field for theft or sabotage. Breathless moments of near discovery rushed at us like express trains, like them flickered past and disappeared. We could manage our lives, it was evident, perfectly well without nannies.

Quite suddenly, around four-thirty, the thing began to pall, became dull, and even frightening. Peggy and Hamer fell out about where we were to go next. We had stones in our socks and were thirsty. Mothers and nannies, resolutely refusing to be panicked, had combed the little town for us; the beach, the rocks, the houses of friends; had almost, but not quite because that would have been feeble, called in the police. On our return home Hamer, most unfairly, played a trump card. Bitterly reproached for tormenting his mother with anxiety at such a time, he burst into most uncharacteristic tears; a circumstance that so stunned his camp-followers that they remained dry-eyed with shock. We were put, exhausted and pugnacious, to bed, with no bedtime story. Hamer at least, the aunts said, is sorry for what he did. Alethea and I resented this. We too could have cried with the best if anyone had put their minds to making us. Broad daylight flowed in through the open window and from across the landing came the sound of Hamer being read to out of *The Children of the New Forest*.

'Nanny, why? Why is Hamer having a story and not us?'

'Hamer at least', Nanny repeated like a dirge, 'is truly sorry for what he did. How you could do such a thing and frighten your dear mothers as you did passes my understanding. But Hamer at least was truly sorry. Settle down now, and go to sleep, and let's hear no more.'

Next morning, Hamer was his usual unchastened self and harried everyone off his private sycamore tree in an amiable but decided manner. A week or so later he led us into a prolonged gang warfare on the beach against another family, called, I think, Warner, one of whom ended up as a captive, held down on the beach while Peggy, ruthless and elegant already at eight years old, painted his face with red Sidmouth mud to make it look like blood and undermine the morale of his sisters. On Sundays, registering sweetness and light, we went to morning service in the parish church, white sailor suits or starched muslin surmounted by roseleaf English complexions. Crisply worded memorials to military forbears frowned down upon us. Across the aisle sat the Robins brothers, Iain, Arnold, Alastair and Angus, sons of the Scots doctor. Worthy opponents; but they were too nice and we knew them too well. Besides they wore the kilt, a uniform against which some instinct warned us that it is inadvisable to gang up.

Also on Sidmouth beach this summer Jack Slessor briefly sat, far apart, with his head in his hands, staring at the pebbles. He was eighteen, of military age; after long and searching attempts to take part in the war, he had been turned down, on account of his polio leg, as unfit for any form of military service. He was a strong and well-made young man, with a not very noticeable limp; someone had thought fit to send him a white feather in an envelope. There was no need for our considerate mothers to urge us not to go and talk to him; his furious despair was something one could feel from twenty yards away. He had always been a formidable figure; he seemed now to have transferred into some sombre adult world. He said absolutely nothing, rose to his feet shortly afterwards and limped away with an expressionless face. At just about this time the Royal Flying Corps, later to become the R.A.F., was called into being. It was not passionately particular about the limbs of anyone who could *fly* and was prepared to fight in the air, in contraptions held lightly together with glue and string, and Jack with the aid of a little intelligent nepotism got himself determinedly into it.

War hung over all of this summer, over the coolness of the sea, the red reflected cliffs, the green fields, the late Georgian elegance of the Sidmouth sea-front; a sort of palpable long-faced gloom, hushed-up but somehow evident. Our mothers seemed to mind things that they used not to mind; laughed less, held long abstracted conversations with one another. Their eyes, seeing us, seemed not quite to focus. There were no more cheerful rowings in boats along the coast to Branscombe or to Ladrum Bay, no fathers or uncles, no male fun, or male games, or male discipline. There was a tenseness, an agonized waiting, while the terrible death-rolls of the western front swelled and mounted, spilled over the newspaper pages into column after column, were read with a riveting fear and horror by those who were still lucky enough to be untouched. Two Hayter cousins were killed; Maurice de Rougement, and Christopher Wrigley, who had been a smiling figure in field boots helping to shake down chestnuts for us last autumn; and it seemed completely unreal. Yet it chiselled mysteriously away at some part of one's being, this death of a generation, this dissolution of a world of laughing and hopeful young men, of kind and stalwart older ones. It lived with one, somewhere in the air, among the buckets and spades and sand, and endless clean linen frocks, and rice pudding and stewed raspberries and Devonshire cream. Facts can always be kept from children but an atmosphere can never be.

Of course there were times when the marble weight that pressed upon our parents' hearts rolled lightly off our own. There were times of rolling over and over on the lawn, speechless with laughter, hours of silent joy among the rock pools, of shouting joy along the sands, of splashing happiness in the sea. There were drives along leafy lanes to play with friends at Ottery St Mary, picnics among the heather of Mutter's Moor, long expeditions up Salcombe and Peak Hill. But even these were nanny picnics; our mothers it seemed were always too occupied at Red Cross classes, sewing parties, hospitals. It was as if they sought, in their anxieties, to separate themselves from us, to hide the war away from our eyes and ears. There were flashing interludes, but basically life was not as it had been.

Concealment of realities was not always possible. I discovered – and at this point the war became completely real – that one was not safe oneself One day I saw in the *London Illustrated News* or it may have been the *Sphere,* a picture of the sinking of the *Lusitania* which altered sharply and for ever my views upon ocean travel. The picture was drawn vividly, probably with a view to stirring the Americans out of their calm. It certainly stirred me out of mine. It showed the huge towering bulk of the liner, leaning at a terrible angle over the struggling figures in the water whom it must soon overwhelm. More struggling figures had attempted to escape through the scuttles and got stuck; their faces were contorted with terror and despair. This picture clamped itself upon my imagination. The ladder up into the bright blue sky wobbled slightly, the crystal railway platform became a thought less solid. My vision of the cosmos underwent a sudden lurch like a ship coming out of harbour and encountering a rough sea. There's a home for little children above the bright blue sky, sure enough; but what about the process of getting there?

The baby in Hamer's family was born and to his gratification it had had the good sense to be a boy. Of seraphic appearance, and christened David, it appeared to afford the aunts even more joy than babies habitually did. Pleasure over this had hardly subsided before his father was killed and my mother amazed me by weeping in the dentist's waiting-room about it. Morale was restored by my seventh birthday which immediately followed on. She gave me a Bible and started to read me a chapter every night. We had previously had Hole's

Illustrated Gospel every Sunday, accompanied by some gripping Old Testament tales out of a small blue book, but the nightly Bible was promotion indeed. Listening to it I felt momentous, grown-up, and very slightly braver; I began to feel part of what was evidently the winning gang. We read, over the years, clean through the Authorized Version and out the other end. Then we began again. Some of the more technical parts of Leviticus may have been left out, but in general no one begat anyone without me being put in the picture. I was and am very grateful for this, quite apart from the spiritual side of it; for being assumed to be old enough, for not being talked down to, fobbed off with a prettified version, for being shown human beings as they really are. All the Bible images fell pat upon my mind. I knew the flocks of sheep and the flocks of much more intelligent goats, the rareness of green pastures, the grateful return from the desert to the sown, the shadow of a great rock in a weary land. I lived among long-robed men who girded up their loins to run, and the fact that in so doing they frequently revealed crimson socks made in Lancashire and yellow sock-suspenders made in Japan did not really shatter the image. If I had been brought up wholly in England, where all pastures are for ever green and the lack of living streams is never felt, the Bible might perhaps not have had so powerful an impact. Living where I did, the Authorized Version seemed to me not only perfectly beautiful but also absolutely real.

The day of embarkation for Egypt came nearer and nearer. I

was now, not without cause, extremely frightened of the sea. An unaccountable niceness crept into my manner for about ten days before the voyage: I was propitiating some sombre powers known only to my instincts. Alethea basked in unexpected kindlinesses, Nanny was dumbfounded by my docility. The dreaded morning came. My mother was not of a nature to allow a passing thing like unrestricted submarine warfare to deflect her from her plan of life – winter spent with her husband, summer spent with her son. In stony apprehension I followed along. The news was increasingly doleful. The P. & O. liner *Persia* was sunk, and the *Arabia,* famous for its cockroaches, horrifically soon after we had voyaged in them. The sinkings seemed to be creeping nearer and nearer to us. Then the *Moldavia* went, and the favourite ship, the *Maloja,* the ship of my fifth birthday. The deck steward in the *Persia* had been a universal favourite; true to type he had been last seen helping passengers into lifeboats with unruffled charm and efficiency. I hoped very much that I too would run true to type and not CRY, but I felt pretty certain that I should. The island race, we all know, does not cry at shipwrecks, whatever its age or sex; but above the thud of racing footsteps, the roar of escaping steam, there would be, I feared, an unmistakable sound of wild boo-hooing. I would try to pretend that it emerged from Alethea, or from Unity Holden or Margaret Greaves or someone younger and feebler of that kind, knowing all the while that in fact it emanated from me.

Our departure from Marseilles this autumn of 1915 in the troopship *Leicestershire* was particularly chilling. From the dimly lighted quay a chaplain addressed the listening men, who leant on the rails of the ship in creditable silence and attention. He may have said many things to help and encourage, but one terrifying sentence sank into my mind. There may be, he said, even now, an enemy submarine waiting for you just outside the harbour. This comfortless prognostication may have been intended to summon the troops to repentance, but it splintered the few remaining nerve-ends of mine that the picture of the sinking *Lusitania* had left intact. As a troopship, we were of course an exceptionally legitimate target. The siren sounded mournfully and ominously as we slid out into the calmness of the dark Mediterranean. It was almost a relief when the crash came.

It was a pitch dark night off the coast of Italy, perhaps at about ten; anyway the grown-ups had come to bed. There was that terrible, rending, deathly, crumple that denotes a collision at sea. I woke out of a light uneasy sleep to the sound of it. It seemed to me that it could only be the painfully awaited torpedo or mine. The ship shuddered all over, like a living thing; and stopped. There were cries from children, and women calling; there was running and stamping and to-ing and fro-ing; banging of doors and the wild roar of the letting-off of steam. Then came what seemed to me a sharp and lethal lurch. As Nanny and Ena fastened our life belts over warm clothes my heart very slowly returned from the position it had taken up just under my uvula and resumed its station to the left of my chest. At the wash handstand, my mother, with care, concentration, and deliberation, was collecting her geranium cuttings and putting them into a sponge-bag. This unselfconscious action could hardly have been more reassuring. There could not be anything very dreadful about a shipwreck if it was something to which one took the geranium cuttings along. Once lifebelted and on the move, once out of the cabin, the situation began to take on a more cheerful aspect, to become even a sort of picnic. As we stumbled to our boat stations while the din of the alarm sounded, word was passed around that the ship had not been in fact either mined or torpedoed. She had been run into in the darkness by one of the convoy. Both ships were considerably damaged but no one was sinking. We went back to bed; the geranium cuttings were replaced in their sand. One's bunk was an imprisoning anticlimax. I lay and looked at the white painted nuts and bolts above me in a sort of stupefaction. Fear re-inhabited me. That long suspense was now again to be borne.

X

How high and graceful the eucalyptus trees now grew around our house, filling it with their rustling sound, shading it from summer heat. Crescent-shaped grey leaves rasped softly on one another in the cool mornings, gave off after the heat of the day their faint delicious clinical smell. But I had lost my nerve about everything; even their height was a menace, since it made certain they would fall on the house some windy night and crush us all to nothing. Even the leopard skin in the outer hall took on a new and monstrous grin. My father had shot it in the Sudan because it was a man-eater, thought by terrified villagers to house an evil spirit. And if it had once held an evil spirit, why not again? Spirits, as everyone knew, were immortal. There's a wicked spirit, hovering round you still, the hymn glumly pointed out; and if there was, why shouldn't he hover round inside a convenient leopard? Night after night I lay rigid within my mosquito net, which had once seemed a protection against the larger fauna but now no longer felt that way, gazing out at the door into the lighted hall, against which I knew that at any moment that terrible square head would loom. Anything was better than being shut into the dark with the whispering trees outside waiting to fall, and Nanny's dressing-gown over the chair taking on every moment more convincingly the shape of a crouching gorilla. God and his angels seemed infinitely far away in their jewelled city, they had pulled up the ladder and shut the door. The trams from wicked Em-baba rolled grumblingly over the Zamalek bridge, squeaked fascinatingly round the bend as they struck land, rocked and flashed with gathering speed down the Boulac road, which lay across dark gardens full of sleeping beasts. Take not Thy Holy Spirit from me, I prayed, miserably, but I could not hear the answer above the violent racing of my heart, and the forty thieves had got off their tram and were climbing into the house up the bignonia creeper. In the stillness of the gardens they crept among the jacarandas and the golden mohrs, under the trees with flowers like scrambled eggs, the trees with fruit like miniature oranges, the trees with leaves like ferns. Under the poinsettias, under the rubber trees, the prowling wild beasts were rousing at darkness from their lairs, and I was no more a clean little girl in a night gown between linen sheets; washed, redeemed, and vaccinated; I was hairy, dirty, and naked; crouched in helpless terror at the back of a cave in the shuddering dawn of time.

England was lion-proof, an island, surrounded by splendid plunging acres of rough seas. Gezira too was an island, but the lions had but to walk from central Africa and cross into it by any one of its four bridges. I dreamed everlastingly of lions, dark blue lions, submarine-shaped lions, preternaturally long and thin and heraldic. Seen from the rooftop in the moonlight they circled unceasingly round our house, sleepless, tireless, hemming us in for ever. Lean and terrible, they paced up and down, round and round and round our house, as I had seen them tirelessly pace their cage at the Giza zoo. They knew no rest, they circled endlessly. And in the end the house would sink and we would go down, down, down among them, and they would get us. In my sleep I gnashed my teeth and cried out loud, and by day I bit my nails and was disagreeable to Mohammed and forgot to feed the rabbits.

'Have you tried bitter aloes?' Ena asked Nanny, and Nanny mercifully shook her head in superior wisdom. But in the evening there she would be, after my bath, with the bottle of syrup of figs, deaf to argument or protest.

'But Nanny, I hate it.'

'Come along, now. Be a good girl.'

'But I hate it. Don't you understand, Nanny, I HATE SYRUP OF FIGS.'

'Come along now. It's only a mouthful and soon over.'

'I shan't, won't, shan't.'

'Think of all the brave soldiers fighting for you in the trenches,' Nanny meanly said. 'Come on, now. Think of the brave sailors out at sea.'

'I don't care. I don't care. I DON'T CARE.'

'Don't care', Nanny said, 'was made to care. Come on then. I'm not standing here all night.'

'But, Nanny, I don't *like* it.'

'I fancy the soldiers in the trenches don't like it either. We do as we have to do. Come now, only a spoonful. I wouldn't want to have to fetch your mother.'

I didn't want that either. She would coax it down in a

moment of calm authority, and what I really wanted was a screaming match, a scene, a dust-up; Nanny's troubled look, Ena's shocked face, Alethea sitting up round-eyed in bed, and a loud yelling release of piled-up nervous tension, with Mohammed and Ahmed running up in case it was a scorpion. And I hoped that all the soldiers and sailors would hear me and be horrified at what they were defending from the Turks in the Sinai Peninsula.

'Come on then, now. Fussing won't make any difference. We do as we have to do.'

Afterwards came the rhythmic soothing sentences, the lull and swell of the Authorized Version, my mother's kiss, and a kind of calm. And then once more the darkness, the tram flashes revealing crouching monsters, the easeless dodging in and out of sleep.

Morning dawned in a hectic gaiety of safety and relief. Kites and crows quarrelled harshly in the sparkling air, from the small birds in the bohinnia trees came waterfalls of song. Hoopoes, with crests like rainbows, strutted on the lawns. With shouts of joy we rushed into our parents' room in the wake of Mohammed bearing their early morning tea, as if the night was gone for good, as if day could, by some miracle, last for ever. After exhausting a considerable capacity for rides and tunnellings, for fun with pillows and eiderdowns, one settled to stories, or to being taught the names of English flowers by my mother out of an old-fashioned illustrated book of hers in which nasturtiums were still called Indian Cress. Alethea was very good at this game. 'Polyampus!' she would shout, at the appropriate page, 'Canterbelly bells!' It was all very soothing. My father would tell us rather less soothing stories out of his life; adventures in the Sudan, smuggling stories learnt when he was a boy on his summer holidays at Lulworth from the Williams family of fishermen – they still remembered the time when excise men were held by their heels over the cliff above Durdle Door until they swore not to tell who the smugglers were. Along in the nursery there were the silkworms, indefatigably cocooning themselves, the singing of the canary, and a comforting row of dolls and animals lolling in their cots, Esky, Robin, Violet and Jack. Out of the window stood the Pyramid of Khufu, foursquare in the morning glitter, behind the shine and tremor of the Nile. Three pyramids in one pyramid, solid, immovable and everlasting, like God the Father, God the Son, and God the Holy Ghost.

The calm static routine of a nursery childhood gradually asserted itself. Sun streamed in through the window of the sewing-room, there were fish-cakes for breakfast, Ena would find a tall stranger in her tea-cup. With luck it would be a brown sock day and not a white sock day, a day of no music lesson, a day of no dentist in Cairo. Before school it was essential to dash out into the garden, to tear round it at full speed, released from the appalling inactivity of a night in bed; to stop suddenly and take in its full delicious leafiness, its dewy freshness, to wash nightmare out of one's being with the sparkling calm of the morning, with the brilliance of light and shade on freesias, phlox and plumbago, with the darkness of hibiscus leaves. By the stone pond papyrus grew, like green umbrella spokes; how had the old Egyptians made paper out of it? The rock garden was built of glittering quartz; asparagus ferns streamed out of it like waterfalls, the clusters of maidenhair fern were cool and river green. The shade was deep and blue, but the garden was all the same shadowless; all was sun, dew, birds, darting blue-tailed lizards, and the smell of mignonette varied by shafts from the kitchen window where my parents' breakfast was being cooked alongside the rather more racy repast enjoyed by the household.

Nanny and I, bearing each other no malice for last night, would set off for school under the leboc trees, to be overtaken by Hugh and Mervyn on bicycles, fortunate individuals who being boys were allowed to go to school unaccompanied. All the trees were now full-grown, spreading and shady, along the Giza and Boulac roads as well as throughout Zamalek. The French and English made, we may be sure, many colonial mistakes; but what they did do was to plant, water, and zealously defend from goats and delinquents, superb avenues of shady trees by those roads along which the poor had for countless years toiled under the remorseless sun; avenues now mostly cut down by indigenous rulers so that the cars of the rich and powerful can go faster.

Mervyn had just learned to bicycle backwards, and gave a demonstration while crossing the Boulac Road. 'If you were in my charge –' Nanny said, but she enjoyed his prowess all the same. Once a man in the turmoil of hashish came running at us from the Boulac Road. His eyes were blank and wild and he uttered unintelligible sounds and took violent hold on

Nanny and pushed her back against the wall of the Sirdaria garden. Nanny retaliated with spirit, and Mervyn and Hugh and I kicked the hashish addict cautiously and ineffectively in the shins through the folds of his galabieh with the sharp edges of our sandals, and he lurched over sideways and recovered himself and made off. This should have been a traumatic experience but was somehow not. Nanny had a sturdy west country resilience and had always expected the Egyptians to behave like that anyway and was therefore unsurprised, and children are quite as often impervious to the truth of danger as they are afraid where no fear is. We went on to school and made a map of the rivers of Spain, the Ebro, the Douro, the Tagus and the Guadalquiver, and Nanny rang up Mohammed to come and escort her back in case the hashish addict was still about, but he was not.

The shadowy Ronnie Grahams had left the house opposite to us, and it was now occupied by Tommy Russell, chief of police, a charming and fearless character later famous for his anti-narcotics activities and known as Russell Pasha. Once, in the 1919 troubles, when the army had been given orders by mistake to fire on a rioting crowd, he drove his car in front of the guns as the only way to stop them. His wife Dorothea could be seen on pearly winter mornings coping dramatically with plunging Arab horses that no one else could ride, before the admiring gaze of the Egyptian police sergeant now permanently on guard at their front gate. Their children, Camilla and John, seemed abashed by so much dashingness, and were further handicapped in life by having to wear boots for their weak ankles. They had a donkey called Moses that they did not much like riding and that was sometimes taken from them by a daredevil character called Trixie Spong and ridden bareback and back to front all round the polo ground at the Sporting Club, and a formidable elderly nanny who saw life in a dim forbidding light and was generally prophesying doom upon every form of enjoyable activity. Any news communicated by her was sure to cause a great shaking of heads and clicking of teeth amongst all the other panama-hatted nannies seated on camp-stools knitting in the shade of the bohinnia trees.

John Russell, in spite of his spindly legs, was a spunky little boy, but some kind of initiation rite seemed to be called for. Aged around five, he was hauled and cajoled up the rubber tree in the government garden and left in the topmost branches and told to get down without summoning aid from his nanny. A selection committee stood under the tree, Frank Tottenham, Jean Goschen, Dan Barton, Wilfred Russell (no relation) and me.

'He can't hang by his legs.'

We stood in earnest concentration, like a group of circus proprietors wondering whether to take up an option on the purchase of a chimpanzee.

'He can hang by his arms,' Jean said.

The objectors, needless to say, were the male members of the committee.

'But he can't hang by his legs,' they repeated.

'Why should he?' Camilla asked, not unreasonably. This

novel viewpoint, though diffidently advanced, was backed up by Alethea, and prevailed. John, by a rather ungracious 'Come on then', was sworn in.

In the afternoons we wheeled out of the garden on the same old soothing, boring walk. Alethea was now promoted to a kind of upright pram known as a Victoria, Nanny and Ena pushed it alternately on the three-quarters of a mile between our house and the Sporting Club, while I exercised my skill on a new hoop, or clanged its stick pleasurably along the iron railings of the houses which succeeded the open fields of Zamalek. The road narrowed for a little way, as it left the fields and passed between high walls, inside one of which lived Diana Graves, whose father, or perhaps whose uncle, was a poet. The English gardens were laid out with lawns and rose-beds and borders, the Egyptian and Syrian ones, far less haphazard, were laid out symmetrically with wide weedless sandy paths and neat circular beds of salvias and coleus enclosing a single palm tree. Bougainvillaea and bignonia splashed over the walls and verandahs of the carefree English; the local inhabitants, more cautious or knowledgeable, kept their walls clear of these snake-harbouring growths. Near the Gezira Palace was the Post Office and a huge banyan tree said to house a family of cobras, which made stamp-buying more interesting than it usually is. The post office clerks sold exquisite stamps with pictures on them of Egyptian monuments and feluccas, the Sphinx, the Pyramids, the statues of Abu Simbel. The clerks had grand long fingernails to show that they were not really workers, but Nanny was unimpressed,

'Lick the envelopes, dear, not the stamps; you don't know who's been handling them.' The Sporting Club was guarded by an amiable character on a cane chair who looked exactly like Lloyd George and was a general favourite with the Nannies. 'Say good afternoon, Priscilla; don't moon; where are your manners hiding?' Eschewing the glorious pleasures of the Swings, she and Ena would settle on camp stools under the mulberry trees on the edge of the cricket field, or in some dull corner of the polo ground. Their starched belts creaked as they leant forward to pick up their balls of wool from the grass, or to hear the gossip further down the nanny-lane. Some of them still wore velvet caps with streamers, like William's first Nanny had, but ours, more progressively, wore a panama hat with a grey petersham ribbon round it. This winter I was prepared to be almost obedient, to play mild sandy games with Camilla and John, or to make dolls' picnics out of flowers and berries with the dreamy and civilized Clavia Goodman, to watch the shiny ponies rocking round the polo ground and hear the knock of the ball on wood and the cry of hooded crows in the monotonous blue of the sky. The shadows moved around and grew deeper, Nanny Goschen had brought a picnic tea for the four Goschens, they sat squarely round it as we rose to go home. The walk suddenly seemed long, I dragged my hoop behind me, registering distress. 'Feel like early bed, do you?' Nanny asked mockingly. 'Come up then, if you want a ride.' This was enough to send one whistling ahead before such an appalling threat of return to babyhood.

At home the changeless and restoring routine continued;

the washing of feet and the putting on of clean socks and muslin dresses, nursery tea, the descent for the enchanted drawing-room hour with one's parents; cards, bricks, singing, stories, and Cadbury's Tropical Chocolates out of a salmon-coloured tin. I had taken at first hardly to literature, preferring occupations at once more active and more mentally lazy. My parents disregarded these tastes and read steadily on until in time I became infected by their pleasure. This winter my father was reading me *Treasure Island,* an unlucky choice, but he had no idea how frightened I already was without all those ghoulish goings-on in the *Hispaniola.* We sat together in a very large armchair, he as much enthralled by the tale as though he had been reading it for the first time. I accepted most of it with a delight that very nearly equalled my alarm, but my nerve cracked when we came to Ben Gunn. At bed-time I could scarcely get past the door into the outer hall, so certain was I that poor Ben Gunn would emerge from the smoking-room, bent double and uttering his haunted cries. Boiled chicken in the nursery, boiled fish, beef broth, steamed brains but nothing fried, never any cheese or spice or olives; but no one worried about the richness of our literary diet.

In spite of pirates, there was something wonderfully static and peaceful about this drawing-room time. No telephone rang, and there was no cocktail hour. At seven-fifteen the dressing-gong sounded, and dinner at eight was cooked by the cook. Our parents were wholly our own. The wood fire crack-led in the grate, the shadow of the standard lamp fell across the green carpet. If one stuck one's legs in the air while being read to, their shadows across the shadow of the lampstand made the letter H. H for Hayter, so right and clever. I surrendered to the beautiful dullness and sameness of the routine. Slowly the dark bird of fear that sat on the bough above my head unfolded his great wings and flapped off harmlessly into the middle distance. It would be months before spring and another journey came.

But even on Egypt, even over fortunate families like ourselves whose fathers in their late forties were too old for military service, the war cast its gloom. The Turks, still held but not driven back, were just across the Suez Canal in the Sinai Peninsula. In the Residency, Sir Henry MacMahon, now High Commissioner, was writing that letter to Sherif Hussein of the Hejaz which was for ever afterwards to make the Arabs feel sure that they had been promised Palestine as a reward for fighting the Turks, and the English feel equally sure that they had not. Far too often my mother would disappear to work in a canteen or the hospital; there were Red Cross classes, and one afternoon, hideous indignity, I was even undressed and put to bed and wrapped by a series of eager and inexperienced ladies, headed by Mrs Ireland in whose house this took place, in many-tailed bandages.

'This way, I *think*, don't you?'

'Or would you say *under*, rather than *over*?'

'Don't let's argue, but I do think . . .'

'According to the *book*, we ought to . . .'

A sullen patient, I felt that freedom could be bought too dearly. I could hear other people playing Robin Hood in the

Blunts' garden across the road. Why me? They were pulling the sheets out from under, any minute now they might start on a blanket bath, and quite honestly I'd as lief have the Turks.

My father seemed to have far too much evening work; it encroached on the sacred hour before bed. 'Go away beastly Committee! Go away fell fiends!' I would shout down through the cork-carpeting in the day nursery, as if the feeling, if not the words, could reach down to the men assembled in the room below, as if my impatience and enmity could blow them to the four winds. No longer did my parents come into the night nursery to show themselves off before dining with the Sultan in the Abdin Palace, she beautiful in a long sweeping dress of corn-coloured satin that set off her dark hair and eyes, he splendid in white tie and khedival orders that were always irreverently known as Nile boils; their joy and pride in one another flashing from them like beams from a lighthouse.

Ahmed left, to learn to drive military vehicles, a progressive and unseemly action that was frowned upon by his father Mohammed. Ahmed's mother had been an Egyptian, he was much lighter-skinned than his Berberine father, and extremely intelligent. 'Of course he must better himself,' my mother said, 'but we shall never have such a good second suffragi again,' and she was quite right, we never did. 'He will get six pounds a month instead of the three we gave him, and a much better future,' my father said, when Ahmed went; but all the same Mohammed drooped without him, and looked somehow older and deflated. 'He won't be in the fighting,' my father said, 'or leave Egypt. It's not in the terms of his engagement. He will drive a lorry, and prosper, and grow great.' But Mohammed refused comfort. The place of a son was by his father, and money, in this connection, was no object. It is much to be hoped that Ahmed still is, somewhere in the new Egypt, a successful garage proprietor in his early seventies, seated on a much too small cane chair outside his house in the cool of the evening, the heir to his father's benignity, his father's stately bulk.

Very surprisingly, the war even brought Jack Slessor, hitherto always a part of summer, of life in England. He had been flying his string and cardboard R.A.F. plane over the Turks in the Sinai Peninsula and machine-gunning them, and over the Dervishes in the Darfur province of the Sudan, who had declared for the Turks and were attacking in support of them. They had retaliated by shooting him in the leg, but his machine mysteriously floated on. Which was as well. Had he survived a crash his end would have been disagreeable and prolonged, the Turks and the Dervishes regarding aerial warfare, unless exercised by the Germans on their behalf, as sacrilegious and not quite cricket. He had killed the white Bishareen camel that Ali Dinar, the savage and tyrannical ruler of Darfur, was riding in the battle, while Ali Dinar was on it, without managing to kill Ali Dinar himself; an action regarded by Alethea and me, and indeed by Jack himself, as a piece of inexcusable gaucherie. Ali Dinar was soon afterwards killed by his own followers, amidst universal relief, and this bit of the war ended, but the white Bishareen camel had been gathered to its fathers and this made the war seem very melancholy indeed.

The bliss of life had slowly, through these calm times, returned to me, but now the days were heating into spring. February was over, and the hamseens, the grilling dusty winds of March, were setting in. Departure loomed ahead, the dreaded voyage must be made. A natural protestant, it is very strange that I never made, or thought of making, any protest. I could have stayed behind in Egypt with my father, though my mother was much more afraid for our health in the summer heat than she was for our lives endangered by submarines. The sea, much as she disliked it, held no very grave terrors for her. Her trust in God was too complete. She died, as she had always supposed she would, peacefully of old age in her eighty-sixth year; the Germans, Nazi or otherwise, could not be supposed to affect the issue either way. Even if I had been given the choice I doubt whether I would have stayed with my father and let my mother go. He seemed to me omniscient, omnipotent, extremely good company, slightly alarming, uproariously funny, and altogether a home edition of God the Father, but I would always in preference have gone with my mother, such being the nature of small children. The father is the sun in splendour, but the mother is the earth in which our roots are planted, from which our life is drawn.

There are some fears so griping, so entwined in one's being that they can never be told. They do not live in words or thoughts, in neat communicable phrases. They are a clutch at the heart, a shadow across the sun. They are unnameable, as if one were a primitive being in thrall to some ancient and hor- rific god, as if one were a naked tribesman in a jungle who would never pronounce the word that means tiger. I was far from being inarticulate, and had plenty of evidence that my parents were both sympathetic and understanding. I remem- bered perfectly clearly how my father, taking William by the hand, had led him into every room in the house one evening, from the basement upwards to the roof, opened every cup- board, looked with him under every bed, gone even into that cool and sinister place, the linen room, to assure him that there was not, as William so firmly supposed, a pack of wild dogs concealed about the house. I myself had suffered from that well-known complaint, wolves under the bed; had told my parents about it as well as the Holy Ghost, had been relieved of it. But there the sea was; my father could not take me by the hand and show me that there were no submarines in it. Quite apart from the logic of the situation, my terror of drowning in a sinking ship was something that I was inca- pable of uttering. The God of light had gone behind a cloud, the old deities of fear and darkness and superstition had me in their gnarled grip. I could only bury terror, and run away from it, and propitiate it in moments when these tactics failed. If I opened my mouth and named it I would be sucked for ever into the swirling darkness of the sea.

XI

March the first was the time-honoured date for giving up the wearing of socks, and in mid-March the increase of heat also brought the closing down of school. This was held in the single room of the lodge inside the Westropps' gate, a fair and curly-haired family of five daughters and one son who lived with their parents, and their grandparents the Willcockses, a half-mile or so from Zamalek across the Boulac Road. Here Miss Quibell, a small, bent, middle-aged woman, controlled and taught without any apparent difficulty or fuss a class of about 20 children between the ages of 12 and 5, and including Overton Kershaw, a wild and gangly boy of 11 whose American mother believed in total self-expression. On Thursdays, wearing a dress of natural silk tussore and shoes embroidered with beads, Miss Quibell taught us dancing; the five positions, the polka, the waltz, the lancers; the curtsy, the bow, and the schottische; and, to sober everyone down before the business of the day began, the preliminary march to the tune of 'The Policeman's Holiday'. This event was held in turn in all our drawing-rooms and was sweetened in so far as was possible for the little boys by being followed by a sumptuous tea. At school we all sat at one table. Down the far end Alethea, Dennis Molesworth, Tony de Cosson, Jennifer,

Wilfred and the Westropp twins would, with heavy breathing, be making rows of pothooks, big A, little a, and those curly capital letters then in vogue but never now seen except upon invitations. Somewhere in the middle Jean Goschen, Rettles, Frank Tottenham, Dan Barton and Diana Watson would be slowly multiplying £19 14s. 3d. by 27. Next to them Hugh, Mervyn, Mary Rowlatt and I would be copying 'Tiger, Tiger, burning bright' off the blackboard, with a view to learning it by heart for homework. At the top of the table Clavia and Overton and Judy McLaughlin and others would be in process of instruction by Miss Quibell into the rudiments of the French Revolution. Latin and French were not included; science, apart from botany and astronomy, never raised its ugly head, and the whole process only lasted for two hours of every morning. Even this was interrupted by twenty minutes break for drinking milk, swinging on the Westropps' swings, worshipping their unresponsive guinea-pigs who lived in a wire-netting cage under a spreading bamboo tree, and chasing each other round Sir William Willcocks' cineraria borders with fatal effects on the flowers at the corners of them.

The most surprising thing about this system was that it worked. Schooled only for less than half the year, all the small boys on leaving Miss Quibell went straight to the top of their prep-schools like hot knives through butter; got scholarships, sailed into universities. Nor did the girls do worse. They had been taught the one essential – how to learn. They had also been induced to want to learn more. They had too – perforce – learned to concentrate; to shut their ears to what went on all round. Miss Quibell, though a dear good woman and a very intelligent one, was without a single charm to help her, a single grace of person or of manner. She sought no favours and made no favourites. She simply taught, and everyone loved her. Her authority was unquestioned; even Overton hung his head with shame before her. Her brother was an Egyptologist, a curator of the Cairo Museum, and behind her lurked all the mystery and prestige of those high cool halls peopled by enormous looming Pharaohs, glittering with sarcophagi, spine-chilling with craggy mummified Rameseses. She insisted upon good writing, neatness, carefully ruled margins, and good manners; seemed never to exasperate or to raise her voice, and gave, guardedly, a measure of praise where praise was due.

Oleanders rustled faintly outside the schoolroom, inside was the delicious smell of cedar-wood while Miss Quibell sharpened our pencils with her small and very keen knife. In the break for elevenses Celia Westropp rather anxiously stood on the path by her garden, in which Sir William Willcocks was bedding out some plants with bright blue flowers. Liking his grandchildren to have gardens of their own, he could not quite resist organizing what went in. 'This is phacelia,' he said, with satisfaction.

'What's for Lena?' the other twin not unreasonably wanted to know. There were, it appeared, some pink ivy-leaved geraniums. The rest of the school, interestedly rubbing the polish off the toes of their shoes by scraping them along the stone edgings of the gardens, were left with the impression that Lena had mysteriously been done down by her grandfather's inability to produce a plant called phalena, and stood around condemningly while he planted the geraniums.

Nothing, now that school was over, to divert one's mind, as the days before the voyage slowly passed. Once again I sacrificed to my outlandish gods, agreeing without argument to a walk in the New Gardens, consoling Alethea over an accident to Affa-Caffa, even passing the sugar to Ena at teatime and altogether behaving in a manner that caused Nanny constantly to take my temperature because it seemed so unlikely. The train rolled out of Cairo station and flew far too swiftly past the willow trees and the yoked oxen of the delta, past the saggias, and the threshing floors, and the canals. The saving solidity of the Port Said waterfront receded, and the Mediterranean stretched endlessly ahead. To avoid the submarines that haunted the normal shipping lanes the ship went round by Crete. The mountains seen from the sea looked harsh and high; one could imagine the Minotaur bellowing among them, and Saint Paul, arguing with the crew and the centurion about where to winter along the steep coast, in one of those passionately involved middle-east arguments in which everyone present takes part at the pitch of their lungs, and which are probably the origin of democracy. But I knew that I must not think thoughts. I must run races, play games, eat large meals, do puzzles, tease and be teased and shout loudly, in case I started thinking of the shuddery fathoms underneath. Noisily, I showed off as a fast runner, challenged everyone to races, thundered continually along the decks, knocking into the deckchairs of unhappy passengers with yellowish faces and steamer rugs, trying to concentrate on *Plain Tales from the Hills*. Whenever occasion arose I made loud mocking jokes about submarines and torpedoes, and threw my life-jacket recklessly down the companionway under the feet of long-suffering Goanese carrying trays. 'Hush now, do,' Nanny said, 'and come and sit down for five minutes.' But I hurried from her, to start trouble on the boat deck between two perfectly amicable people who were playing chess there, or to disturb Ena by asking repellent questions such as, Which would you rather, be burnt alive or eat a plateful of live earwigs? insisting doggedly on a definite answer.

Only in the evenings, sometimes, for a moment, was there peace. The Bible was my sheet anchor, and I hung on to it tightly for as long as its strange spell lasted, and never more so than on a particular evening off the Sardinian shore. In the way that frightened children always do hear what will least encourage them, I had overheard someone saying that a ship had been torpedoed two hours behind us, and another ship three hours ahead. So that I knew that destruction would be waiting for us in the night. It was a rough evening and we all felt rather ill. The cabin, in the intervals between waves, was full of stormy light. The waters of the Tyrrhenian Sea, green against the sunset, slapped and banged against the scuttle. The camp stool, upholstered in carpet, collapsed with a sudden clatter. Gathering clouds added to the melancholy menace of a rough evening at sea. The drinking water, beneath its covering tumbler, whooshed in its water-bottle. My mother's dressing-gown, a large green pendulum, swung slowly on its hook. It was my turn for the boring lower bunk; Alethea was already sleeping overhead. Sticky from a salt-water bath, I lay plucking the pleats of my nightgown while I waited for my mother to begin. Made by Nanny, it had an embroidered yoke, and rows of feather stitching between tiny pleats. My mother, undeterred by headache and nausea, read me the story of Joshua, and of the improbable crumbling of the walls of Jericho before the trumpets and the shouting of Israel, a crude and magic tribal tale with the silver streak of faith in a living God running like a vein of ore through it. My mother yawned from time to time ominously with the increasing movement of the ship. But I was part of the shouting trumpeting army and whatever my shortcomings I belonged on the side of God and it was comfort and calm. The German submarine commander, rocking in wait in the waters of the Tyrrhenian, probably felt exactly the same, but this particular issue was never put to the test; he missed us, and we tied up alongside safely at Marseilles.

Here a shock awaited us. In addition to tickets and French money, my mother had twenty-five golden sovereigns with her. During our voyage from Port Said, the French Government had issued a decree forbidding the export of gold; an ordinance interpreted so literally by the customs officers at Marseilles that they took away my mother's sovereigns the minute she stepped ashore, substituting what appeared to me to be a pile of crumpled and dirty paper. The war on the western front was not at this time going well, cries of '*nous sommes trahis'* were beginning to roll round France. My mother's objections to the removal of her gold were curtly met. Her command of foreign languages was never notably exact. She was apt to talk French at Zagazig in the delta, and to startle the porters at the Gare du Nord with a sudden flow of Arabic. She protested haltingly and in vain. Her arguments were overborne by characters with blue chins and the abrupt and menacing manners of the Midi, and her beautiful shining sovereigns were all taken away. How lucky that William was not a witness to this event; he could never have entered the Foreign Service if he had been.

Furious and helpless, I stood by. 'Steady, now dear,' Nanny said, holding me firmly by the shoulders. She was quivering with Anglo-Saxon indignation herself. I instantly forgot the kindness of the blue-bloused porter who had rescued my collar box from under the train, of the concierge at Lyons who had come running after the train with my lion, and roughed myself over with that strong allergy that has caused the English and the French, two nations so intelligent, lively, and valuable, so necessary to each other and to the world, to spend six or seven hundred years dinging and banging away at each other.

On the way to the station from the dockyard the wheel came off our vehicle and it ground to a halt on the cobbles. Pieces of luggage toppled slowly off the roof and rolled away, the two horses stood panting dejectedly in the path of an oncoming tram, which tinged wildly and drew up with a screech. A large crowd instantly collected and gave rein to a flow of unfavourable comment upon the English; their excessive luggage (so cruel to horses) *'ah, ces pauvres bêtes'*; their habit of travelling in wartime through other people's countries, thus impeding the war effort that the French alone were making; the grave and obvious lack of English prowess in the field. I could understand, but not reply; but while the others were collecting the scattered cases and soothing the tramdriver with largesse, I turned round and made the rudest possible face at the French, coupled with a noise I had learnt from Egyptian boys that was understandable in any language. It was not much, but it was relieving.

We had rather a shaken breakfast at the Terminus Hotel, during which Nanny was conspicuously sympathetic and kind to my mother, who obviously felt slightly raped, and longing for my father to be there, with his capacity to soothe, pacify, reason with, and finally outwit the French.

Crestfallen and depressed, we climbed the steep steps into the Paris express. 'You should know better', Nanny said, 'than to lose your temper in front of foreigners.' The train settled to a fast even rhythm, the river Rhône leapt and sizzled past the carriage window. On the spirit lamp from the tea-basket, Ena methodically boiled the French germs out of our milk. 'This time two days,' Nanny said, 'they'll be drinking proper milk.' Bred in the west country, she was a pasture snob. The Rhône gave place to the slow and poplar-fringed Saône, calm and beautiful in the fading spring light. In the morning there was the Seine, flowing the other way, the Mediterranean world had ended, the Atlantic world begun. Our spirits rose to meet the windy challenge of it. Paris already was plastered with that unlikely Savon Cadum baby, and even in the teeth of a terrible war retained its characteristic smell of coffee, urinals, plane trees, French cigarettes, sophistication, and newly baked bread. In the hotel there were yellow satin chair seats and a delectable breakfast, 'No coffee for me, thank you, Madam, it's too indigestible.' There was even time for a visit to the Jardin des Plantes. The night crossing from Le Havre in a crowded darkened ship with the passengers commanded to keep their lifebelts on, brought us to the cold early morning quays of Southampton, to primroses in flower along the railway embankments, fat lambs in the emerald fields; to the just beginning green of beechwoods, to the rains and the rations and the sharp winds of spring.

England was tenser and bleaker than ever before, with many wounded men in the streets, less singing and whistling at street corners, and a look upon lined adult faces of being locked in a death struggle; a weary doggedness, a totally committed grimness. This was the summer of Jutland, the summer of the Somme. The familiar faces of Aunt Ag and Aunt Bay were wreathed in long black widows' veils which trailed out behind them as they walked. 'Tedious things!' Aunt Bay said, and sensibly took hers off at the first opportunity and went up to London to pay some jolly visits. 'Bay loves *gadding*,' the other aunts said, but you could see they didn't grudge it to her. Uncle Beachy, not without savoir-faire, had lost his life in France. Thus redeemed in Slessor eyes, he could be mentioned again, was allowed to be regretted, mourned, almost looked on with affection, readmitted to the fold. 'He was in some ways a bad lot,' Aunt Bay admitted, about forty-five years later, 'but I loved him, and we had fun together.'

She herself lived to be ninety-three, extremely active and enjoying all but about the last ten minutes.

The Sidmouth sand was chill and red after the warm silvery Egyptian kind, and although we dug and castled it with undiminished enthusiasm and further depleted the shrimp population in the rocks, William on his holidays seemed to join less wholeheartedly in these ploys, seemed to have moved away into a different and more complicated world. He read a great deal and was much more silent. Hamer had gone to Lynehams and had his hair cut very short; he was now fatherless and if possible tougher than before; he had a pistol with caps and eschewed the company of girls and collected birds' eggs and butterflies with ruthless intensity. His older sister Phyllis had gone into permanent stockings, and had her hair tied back with a black bow at the nape of her neck and wore long skirts. She had given up paddling and taken to being nice to babies. Jack Slessor was now flying, Rodney a soldier, and Tony nearly a sailor. Their sister Betty, though still in muslin and chip straw hats for Sunday, spent less of her time on a bicycle and had become interested in clothes. However much one thought one had grown up and become more sophisticated and worldly over the winter, one seemed never to catch up; cousins, like the Joneses, were always a lap ahead. Triumphantly one arrived at where they had been last summer, only to find that they had moved on into yet another more bewilderingly adult world; dazzled one with new speech, ideas, clothes, ploys. It left one out of breath.

That one could live one's life at one's own pace and not bother to keep up, is a solution that does not seem to have occurred, or anyway to have been accepted by me. But this summer fortunately a younger cousin swam, breast-stroke, into my ken; Harry Slessor, a light-hearted character who would never bother with the necessity of growing up a minute before he felt like it. He was proceeding along the shallows of Sidmouth beach with his shoreward foot firmly touching the ground at each stroke. His virtuosity in achieving this without the faintest betraying jerk was remarkable. 'Well done, Hadge darling!' his mother applauded from the bank, 'You're swimming!' Through the heavy splashes of seawater that covered his face Harry contrived an immense conspiratorial wink. 'You're really swimming, darling, isn't that splendid?' Harry naturally made no attempt to refute this statement but proceeded westward with uncanny smoothness. I foxed grown-ups, of course, myself, from time to time; but with not nearly such skill and aplomb, nor with such evident enjoyment. Harry was six, and reputed by his mother, his governess, and his older sister Anne to be very delicate; a medical dictum which failed to discourage him in any way and which, over the years, he effectively disproved.

The beach, glistening with tidal newness, gave back the delicious smell of salty weed drying in the sun. Harry, rising to his feet, disgorged an immense amount of seawater before his laughter became too much for him. From the beach the nannies standing on the edge seemed to be going through the motions of summoning us from the deep, signals that it was impolitic to ignore for too long. One was already so cold as almost to be aware of it, although one would deny, through loudly chattering teeth, any suggestion of chill. The sea was clear and grey and still, its pebbly bed showing up distinctly. How strange that the sea could be so enchanting, so spell-binding at the edges, and so utterly horrific in the middle.

There were fewer signs of war at Sidmouth than there were up country. Devonshire cream still appeared thickly in earthenware bowls, was spread on chudleighs and still lav-ishly covered with blackcurrant or raspberry jam. There was butter and eggs, and a general west country conviction that what goes on in the rest of the country is really neither here nor there. But the two little paddle steamers, the *Duke of Devonshire* and the *Duchess of Devonshire,* no longer called for passengers along the coast at Exmouth and Budleigh Salterton and Sidmouth and Beer, with the gangplank run out into the clear pebbly sea and Bob and Tom Woolley helping the passengers ashore.

A glum farewell to William preceded our final wartime voyage. He was totally and despairingly silent. My mother made her usual heroic bid to rise above the sadness of the hour. The usual clutch of fear crowded out any other emo-tions I may have felt. We left England on my eighth birthday, setting off from Sidmouth station amidst determinedly cheer-ful farewells from the aunts. 'What about my birthday cake?' I asked greedily, but no one seemed to be attending. A new under-nurse called Mary West had replaced Ena, who had been summoned home by her mother's rheumatic fever. She seemed less cosy, in fact rather stiff; and I resented the mole on her cheek. At Ottery St Mary station Ena was on the platform to greet and say goodbye to us with warm splodgy kisses and a red diary for 1917 as a birthday present for me. Ottery St Mary looked very settled and safe; I had a moment of longing to get out of the train and stay there with Ena, specially as she was obligingly crying at our departure.

The ship was a Bibby liner and the passage was a very rough one. On a bright tossing blue day we stopped suddenly in the middle of the Mediterranean, veering about rudderless on what seemed mountainous sapphire waves off which the wind was tearing great fringes of crystal spray. Steam was let off with a roaring nerve-shattering sound, alarms went – what now? There was a long pause when absolutely nothing happened and the ship seemed to turn round and round and even go backwards. This moment of suspense, of nothingness, was somehow more terrifying than anything that had gone before. We seemed to be captainless, to be waiting, without help or guidance, for explosion or sinking. All was unexplained; we simply went on again, and the passengers, with slightly hysterical laughter, came down from their boat stations and continued the shuffleboard tournament.

The rolling creaking days went interminably on, the cotton-woolly apples in the early mornings, condensed milk at tea, hair washing on Friday, 'Eternal Father Strong to Save' at church in the leaping dining-saloon on Sunday, and at night the iron scuttles screwed tightly over the glass ones, the heavy curtains swinging, and the slapping menacing waters always to be heard outside in the heaving darkness of the sea.

Off Greece came a day of calm. From the top bunk one could look out in the early morning and see the line of the horizon, pale, and mingled with pale sky. An occasional welcome island slid by. Like the ancient Greeks I had little confidence in the science of navigation and preferred to stay in sight of land when at sea, and in sight of the sea when on land. Shores of one sort and another stayed visible all day; the rolling of the swell grew gentler; I began to have a secret half-allowed hope that we might even reach Egypt safely. Fear arrived as usual with nightfall. A darkened hunted vessel, we flew like a fugitive far off the normal course. My heart seemed to be holding its breath as we slid along in the gently heaving stillness of a starry night. The ship was a fast one and the danger was not great; my ignorance as usual magnified it.

The regular rhythm of the ship's engines continued. Any minute now, they were saying, any minute now, any minute now. The spent waves hissed along the side of the ship, the swishing grasping water that was waiting to get in and consume us. It would rise higher and higher in the cabin, our heads would bump along the rivets of the ceiling, the lights would all go out, we would die in terrible darkness and fear. My mother opened the Bible and I listened to the sound but not to the sense of her reading; I could not for the moment divorce myself from my fear. The rhythm of the sentences gained slowly on me. After all, they had clamped the scuttles down, so that the water could not, anyway, get in that way. The words of Isaiah flowed gradually over me like an incantation, the rocking lulling sentences were the waves of a kinder sea. My mother's low untroubled voice went on. The sound of the words rose and fell, mysteriously rhymed and chimed, dropped with certitude into their appointed places.

'Hast thou seen that which backsliding Israel hath done?'

Aware of being one who habitually backslid myself, I stopped dwelling in the sound and started to listen to the sense.

'She is gone up upon every high mountain and under every green tree, and there hath played the harlot.'

The beauty of this picture withdrew my attention from the haunting terror outside in the dark night. They had explained to me what a harlot was, but I had forgotten. Clearly, in the context, it must be some kind of musical instrument. Perhaps a mouth organ, or a guitar, or a very small harp? Anyway you played it, backslidingly or otherwise, upon every high mountain. Riding a donkey, in the bright sun, you played it; and the sound went echoing down the valley. You played it under the splashing shade of the cedars. The others can play the harp if they like, or the flute, but bags I play the harlot. The rest of you can sing.

'Return thou backsliding Israel, saith the Lord, and I will not cause mine anger to fall upon you, for I am merciful.'

Under every green tree, playing and singing, with harlot, lute and timbrel; followed by a picnic lunch with stone ginger beer and hard-boiled eggs. A faint breeze stirred the cedars, the lizards flicked through the rocks. The strong air filled my nostrils, the sappy shrubs gave out an aromatic smell in the heat of noon. The stony mountainside was hard underneath me, warm and dry on the calves of my legs. Soon we would have to pack up the picnic and get on the donkeys and go home in the cool of the evening, with the music going with us. The sun was now low and kind in the sky, the shadows falling blue. What tune next? Well, you choose first if you like, but then I choose 'Tipperary', and 'Robin Adair', and 'Little Grey Home in the West'. It's your turn now to play the harlot, and I will play your flute. The stones slid under the donkeys' feet and the noise of the music echoed back from the other side of the valley.

'Turn, oh backsliding children, saith the Lord, for I am married unto you.'

The novelty of this notion jerked me out of my vision. God the Father was understood, but God the Husband? God was married to people. To Lascars. To Nannies. To Egyptian donkey boys. To me. But not, surely, to Turkish prisoners working by the Pongly-Zongly bridge, not surely to Germans? Could all be joined in the loving indissoluble bond in which my parents lived? It was rum, but reassuring.

The Bibby line sheets felt less harshly along the back of my legs, the pillow less brick hard. I stopped counting the painted rivets above my head, in nervous concentration, back and forwards, and up and down, and then all over again. The ship smell died out of my nostrils, the beat of the engines came less clear. Slowly the sun and the sea air gained over the streams of fear that coursed and bubbled through my veins. Two days later, unbelievably, were the roads of Port Said, the ships riding at anchor, little boys shouting and diving from boats, gully-gully men, the blessed noise and warmth and smell of Egypt. And Cairo station, the high autumnal Nile, the trinity of the Pyramids, the shadows of eucalyptus leaves falling on the hot walls of home.

XII

Nineteen-seventeen, a year of destiny for the world, came in after a very cheerful Christmas and a Christmas tree which for the first time I saw to be artificial.

'Why? Why is it made of green paper?'

'We can't get the proper kind any more. They used to come from Austria-Hungary.'

Austria-Hungary, a purple splodge on the map, instantly covered itself in Christmas trees with enemy soldiers lurking behind them. The Emperor Franz-Josef, familiar from the pages of *Punch,* stood astride it with his side whiskers bristling; I mowed him down with my bow and arrow. The war had gone on for far too long, it was getting a bore; people talked and thought about nothing else. The Emperor had, mysteriously, been involved in its having begun at all; along with the Kaiser and little Willie he shared the disapprobation of Nanny and of Mary West, elicited mockery from the soldiers in the newly made camp down the road.

The servants stood around, their faces glistening with pleasure. Stalwart Moslems, they all adored the Christmas tree and would have been deeply hurt not to have received Christmas presents. The house was decorated, failing holly, with red-berried branches from the pepper tree.

'Is that sponge Mohammed has got big enough? It's so very inflammable.' Buckets of water stood in a row. How wonderful it would be if it caught fire! Nothing could be more exciting and beautiful than a Christmas tree on fire. 'Darling what are you doing? Take care! Don't blow the candles like that!'

Alethea had now arrived at an admirable age. Though still rarely allowed to possess an existence in her own right, she was deeply appreciated as a companion. 'You are jolly well five,' I pointed out to her as we stood beside the ranunculus border on her birthday morning. She had paid the subscription and could now be said to have joined the club. She qualified from now on as Little John, or Rebecca; as Sancho Panza, Amy March, or Alan Breck Stuart. Above all, she was admitted to have a half share in the reversion of the soldiers' antelope.

The C. in C.'s camp was just down the road, half-way down what had now come to be called Sharia Ibn Zanki. Huts and stables stood in what had been a field of berseem surrounded by snake grass. We tended to stop there for conversation every afternoon. Nanny had a steady friend who was a photographer and lived in a banana grove off the Pyramid road beyond Giza; she took us to tea there sometimes and he gave us butterscotch and constantly photographed Nanny looking youthful and relaxed under a banana tree; but she was not above friendliness with sergeants. This was a tendency to be encouraged since it enabled one to slope off and hold converse with the horses, champing and whisking in their open stable, and with the antelope. Sitting on a horse's back one afternoon, peacefully being Joan of Arc and meaning no harm to anyone, I was seized off briskly by the corporal in charge and subjected to a hail of righteous indignation from all those present.

'Running away when my back was turned,' Nanny said.

'Backing a stabled horse,' the corporal said.

'If I've told you once I've told you a dozen times,' Nanny said.

'And one that don't know you either,' the corporal said.

'And look at your clean dress,' Mary West said.

'I can't turn my back for two minutes,' Nanny said.

'If you'd tried backing Blackie, just down the line,' the corporal said, 'he'd have half killed you like as not.'

'Clean on this very afternoon,'

'Then you'd have had what for from the sergeant,' the corporal said.

'Leave alone from General Allenby,' Nanny said, 'that you had that nice paint-box off his Christmas tree.'

To and fro they went, like a Greek chorus, back and forth in a self-defeating pendulum of disapproval against whose beat the heart automatically hardens, the lower lip instinctively juts. Soon afterwards the horses left without a stain on their characters, to be ridden in the Palestine fighting, perhaps the last great cavalry campaign of history.

On shorter visits I would stand brooding over the mysterious legend 'C. in C.'s Camp' which the soldiers had picked out in white-washed stones and interplanted with lobelias. C. in C.'s Camp. I knew the Commander in Chief perfectly well, he gave particularly excellent children's parties. He was an enormous kindly burly general called Edmund Allenby, who lived just down the road. His Christmas tree party had been supreme, far jollier than the Residency one, since it was interspersed with wounded soldiers. Nothing connected him in my mind with C. in C. Who *was* this mysterious C., and what was he doing in C.'s camp? And if it was his own camp, why shouldn't he be there anyway? Impossible to ask, and be laughed at by Nanny and the sergeant for my simplicity. It was too late to find out. C. in C.'s Camp. This legend, among its lobelias, puzzled me for weeks.

The soldiers were about to invade Palestine and drive out the Turks, they wanted a home for their antelope where it would be loved and cherished in the style to which it had become accustomed and they offered it to us. Would we make a home for it? This simple request my heartless parents refused to grant. It seemed impossible to understand them. Did they expect the poor antelope to join in the fray and get shot at by the Turks? What *did* they expect? Inconceivable that the fate of the antelope should be a matter of indifference to them. For some weeks now Alethea and I had been alternately Robin Hood and Little John, and it was beginning to pall. The number of nannies down the ages who have been prepared wholeheartedly to take the part of the Sheriff of Nottingham could be counted on the fingers of one hand. Mine treated my skill as an archer with open scorn. Rushing out of ambush round the corner of the house I had come upon her seated twenty yards away in a deckchair, noncha-

lantly knitting, and called on her to surrender. Lacking
English yew, I had a palm branch bow (far too whippy) and
bamboo arrows. 'Aim straight at me', Nanny said, 'and I'll be
safe.' Disregarding all that my father had said on this subject,
I complied. Luckily the bamboo was blunt, and the wound in
her neck was not lethal, but remorse took the edge of joy off
this game, and I had it in mind to be for a while the princess
whose lily-white doe dropped its head right into her hand and
followed wherever she would goe. The antelope, apart from its
native charm, seemed the ideal adjunct. Can't it live in the
potting-shed? There's a huge big box the piano came in that
would just do for its bed? Can't it live in the rose garden? No,
it would eat all the roses, and escape, and be eaten by pariah
dogs itself. Can't it live in the basement? Can't it live on the
roof? It's quite small. I will feed it myself, always, every day,
for ever and ever, and give it plenty to drink, and exercise it,
and clear up after it, and nurse it when it is ill. You are at
school, and out all day, what sort of life will that be for the
antelope? I promise and swear I'll look after it and be with it
always.

It was no use. They were adamant. Oh, the injustice of it!
I made one last try, on Saturday morning at their breakfast,
when there was time to develop the theme. But their refusal
held. I left them alone in their unrepentance and went out
into the garden. Mahmoud was hosing the lawn. Fortunate
being, he was allowed to use the hose, heavy galvanized iron
tubes held together by leather joints which occasionally gave
out a faint spraying leak.

The soaked lawn exuded a pleasing smell which my furious nostrils declined to register. Magnificent arcs of glittering water splayed out from the hose, made by Mahmoud's finger pressure; it was a task allowing unlimited scope for creative artistry. The bare feet of Mahmoud moved in careless freedom through the shallows of the flooded grass. His state was god-like, and was denied me. Never did he wear socks or go to the dentist; he drank dark brown Nile water out of the spout of the watering can and spat food out unhesitatingly whenever he felt like it. My parents would not allow me to use the iron hose. There was all that Nile, and all that garden, and yet they denied me the pleasure; the hose was kept jealously in the hands of Ismaïn and Mahmoud. Too heavy for me to hold? I would have soon shown them. But it was no use. They were eaten up with hard-heartedness, prejudice, and injustice. Tears of anger churned themselves up, and I fed their source enjoyably with bitter streams of thought. In the top of the rubber tree my rage came splashing out.

The antelope now assumed an enormous importance in my mind. It became my scapegoat, my soul, my hope of heaven. It was beyond measure necessary to possess it, to be it, to partake of its innocence and beauty, to live behind its large brown eyes, inside its fawnish skin and its gently heaving flanks. If I had the antelope I could stop being greedy, vindictive, and mean. If I had the antelope I could shed the load, I could go back into the garden of Eden. If I had the antelope I could stop teasing Camilla and John about their weak ankles, could stop hating Miss Simpson who taught the piano for being so mauve and docile and easily offended, could stop scorning the Egyptians for their filth and degradation and their fly-covered faces; could cease to sink, burn, and destroy. If I had the antelope I could live with it in a world where all my impulses would be loving, truthful, and kind. Nothing stood between me and this idyllic state of things but my parents with their besotted preoccupation with rose trees.

I climbed high, higher, out among the thin top branches. They would give way, probably, and I would fall and break my leg, and then my father and mother would see and understand what their harshness had accomplished. Or probably my back. I would lie all day on a sofa, radiating sweetness and patient goodness, like someone in Charlotte M. Yonge, or Cousin Helen in *What Katy Did*. Then, too late, my parents would see the fatal error of their ways. Tormented by remorse, they would scour the plains of Africa, seeking vainly for an antelope. Too late, their eyes would be opened and they would know. I saw them, defeated and exhausted figures, tramping through the grilling wastes of the desert. My mother's long skirts trailed in the sand, my father's sun helmet was sticking to his head with sweat. Lions lay along the branches of those shallow trees that occurred in Uncle Andrew's photographs of Somaliland. Indifferent giraffes, turning their backs upon my parents, pulled off pieces of tree with their long grey tongues. The tips of the lions' tails twitched lazily in the heat of the day. They had eaten all the antelopes themselves. There were none left.

One of the lions turned its head round and revealed itself

as having my father's face. It was laughing, and something in me wanted to laugh back, but I repressed it sternly. Not so easily could such a thing as this be laughed away. The top branches of the rubber tree had long slim salmon-red buds, its leaves were dark green and very shiny. From the Zamalek bridge came the sound of trams rumbling over before the noon opening, of donkey boy cries, of the protests of camels being separated from other camels, of the loud reproofs of their owners. Nobody seemed to be noticing me and the boughs failed to break. My stomach was sending urgent messages of hunger. I climbed moodily down and plodded anti-climactically back to the house for milk and biscuits.

At the back door, under the bougainvillaea trellis which shaded its steps, an unsympathetic group was gathered; Nanny, Mohammed, two Egyptians who brought the blocks of ice, and a Greek woman who boiled my father's stiff shirts.

'Your *socks*!' Nanny said. 'Green as grass.'

'Te kreema!' the washerwoman chipped in sycophantically to rub home the point.

The icemen, aware of nothing but my discomfiture, grinned sardonically. Even the benign seriousness of Mohammed's face wore, in so far as it was in it to wear, a look of reproach.

'Mush kwise,' he said, shaking his head.

This derogatory comment was probably directed at the block of ice, but I instantly appropriated it to myself. Mohammed had, as a rule, a soul above petty feminine recriminations. Et tu, Brute! I felt, but in English.

'Someone', Mary West said, coming down the steps and

joining the group, 'got out of bed the wrong side this morning.'

This hateful pronouncement was too much. I had meditated easing my way back into the comity of nations by telling them all that one of the baby rabbits had opened its eyes, but now they were not going to know this piece of good news. I shook the dust off my feet in a gesture recognizable by speakers of any tongue and passed them by in silence. Half-way up the back stairs a pigeon had made a nest on the wide creeper-shaded stone window-ledge and laid two eggs, carelessly casting down a few sticks, as pigeons do, and trusting to luck to do the rest. It is a miracle that the young of pigeons ever grow up. Stumping grumpily past them, I felt a wave of sympathy with those two eggs.

Harden not your hearts, it said, but I went on comfortably hardening mine for another twenty-five minutes. When actually confronted with my parents it was a much more difficult process to keep up. They were so tiresomely charming and funny and unimpressed. After a bit I could make nothing more of it and was obliged to embrace them warmly. My mother, surprisingly, gave me a new drawing-book and a thimble, as a reward for not going on and on and on about the antelope. I felt as if I *had* gone on and on, or anyway gone on.

The soldiers, disappearing overnight from Zamalek, departed to deliver Palestine as their crusading forbears had so long and vainly tried to do, and the antelope went into the Zoo, or even, terrible thought, into the pot. News of the campaign floated back, there was a general lifting of hearts. T. E. Lawrence, not yet known as Lawrence of Arabia, came and went from Cairo. He and Allenby were as unlike in character to the people depicted in the film, as Lord Cromer was unlike the sketch of him by Lytton Strachey, and that is saying plenty. I never met Lawrence, but many I knew did; lived with, fought with, and worked for him. Their opinions, absorbed over the years, could be summed up in a saying of Gilbert Clayton's – 'He was a truly great man, and don't let anybody ever tell you different.'

Before next Christmas Jerusalem was taken; and one could see on grown-up faces, what that meant. Allenby, by a superbly imaginative and characteristic action, captured for a short while the sympathy of the entire middle eastern world, a region that believes and understands in the language of symbol. Descending from his horse, which in 1917 was an eccentric thing for a cavalry officer to do, he went on foot into the Holy City, feeling himself unable to ride in triumph as a conqueror over ground which Christ had ridden over to die. Allenby was all of a piece; he never did things for effect. He went that way because he felt that way. The effect, all the same, was prodigious, and all the more so as the German Kaiser, arriving to visit Jerusalem previously, had self-importantly caused a special breach in the walls to be made for his entry.

Resigned now to not being the antelope, I could perhaps have fun on other planes of life. Watching the conjuror at the Allenbys' Christmas party I had sat next to a man with one arm in a sling, who had asked me, when applause became necessary, to clap his remaining hand. He was so nice that

I failed to point out to him the fallacy in the arithmetic of this proposition – my other hand left over. I invited him to come home, where he immediately and rather annoyingly seemed to become the property of my parents, to move into that dull old thing of knowing people in England that they knew. My day was to come. I was asked alone and unaccompanied by Nanny or Mary West, to spend the afternoon with him at the Zoo. This attempt of a lonely man several thousand miles away from his own eight-year-old daughter to keep his hand in by going on an exhausting spree with someone else's, was, rightly, taken at its face value. We drove off smartly in a car, a dashing change from the usual slow progress behind horses. Less dashing was my boring white jersey and white serge skirt. They became, it was comforting to note, fairly greened over by animal slobber soon after we reached the Zoo.

The Zoo at Giza was in a paradisal garden once devised by a millionaire pasha for a much-loved wife. Spacious, and shaded by enormous trees, its paths were mosaiced in bright curlicue patterns of black and red and yellow pebbles. First magnet was the lion house, with its powerful savage smell, and yellow-eyed pacing lions, which one longed to let out, and yet trembled thinking of it. The panther, black as night, lay still, his brilliant eyes stared out past craning heads. Little Egyptian boys gibed at him, threw peanut shells in through the bars of the cages, made sudden loud teasing sounds. There were moments when I hated the Egyptians and this was one. When they tore frogs and nestling birds in pieces at wayside railway stations, in order to induce European passengers to give them money to stop doing it; when, out of nothing but love of exercising pride and power, they incessantly belaboured overladen donkeys who were going the right way anyhow as fast as they could manage; or when, as now, they taunted caged lions; I felt for them a deep belly loathing, increased by the known futility of intervention. Nor did I reflect that the Egyptians had been more or less so treated themselves, over the centuries, by the Turks and others, and indeed by their own countrymen, and were not in general more cruel than other people. Generally it was difficult not to like them and sympathise with them, so poor, engaging, voluble, and obtuse; haunted by rank misgivings and sustained by garish hopes unlikely of fulfilment.

We hurried away, past the hippopotamus pool where, so enigmatically, the small hippopotamus was older than the large hippopotamus. William would have known that they were a different species, but William, alas, was not there. The rhinoceros was called, surprisingly, Kitty, and lived with a fat indifferent piebald goat upon whom it doted. Shining with good living, the goat would push the rhinoceros away from the food. The rhinoceros stood humbly by, gazing with sad devotion at the goat's tightly stretched flanks. This was my first glimpse of unrequited love, that glooming spectacle. When the goat finally died of over-eating, Kitty refused all food, and the company of all other goats, and died too, a Juliet among pachyderms.

The giraffe paddock seemed huge, a splendid herd stretched their necks and lolloped around in what was very nearly their native sunshine. No one had been so unkind as to import a polar bear to gasp through the Egyptian summer, but otherwise there seemed to be everything, and we left no stone unturned; visiting birds, reptiles, rats, monkeys, snakes and bats, finishing with a tea far larger and more unhealthy than Nanny would have permitted. How grand it was to tilt one's chair nonchalantly back, talking lightly of this and that, consuming a mass of sticky nutty indigestible cakes and gulping quantities of what was almost certainly unboiled buffalo milk. Heady with freedom, I reached out for yet another gooey Italian cake. The light sloped across the lake where the black and white ducks swam, where cranes and sacred ibis dipped and spread. I could have sat for ever and watched the drops of shining water rolling off their backs. Flocks of white egrets came home from the fields to roost in the safety of the banyan tree; the sunset painted them pale pink. Satiated to the point of near-silence, I sat at ease while the shades of evening fell deeper. I had not yet grasped the idea of saying that it was time to go home. Far away the band had stopped playing and was packing up its instruments for the night. The lions, gorged after their buffalo meal, had ceased to roar. The night birds were tuning their harsh cries. Light had gone from the lake. It was a jungly frightening fascinating world, and even if the lions were all to escape I felt confident that my friend, in spite of his wounded arm, would be able to handle things. In the pepper trees, the cicadas started up. We should probably be there still, but for the closing of the gates.

The walk next day with Nanny felt a sad come-down, and

why would she still not let us go to the Swings? Life on the edge of the cricket ground amongst younger and more biddable children seemed ever tamer and more stuffy, a long cup of weak tea. Boring to lie flat on the grass on one's back and gaze up into the sky, which, for once, was covered in grey mackerel scales of cloud.

'When you look up,' I asked Alethea, 'do you see masses of little grey lines writing themselves and wriggling about in the sky?' But she was playing with Camilla, collecting little bunches of clover and using them for some game of house or other. Surely, life held so many riper ploys. Did no one realize that I was eight, and a woman of the world? From the Swings came lively vicious cries; I could hear an Italian acquaintance shouting at his younger sister in tones and language that Nanny would instantly have condemned. Gang warfare was raging, there were spoiled rich Syrians with pasty faces and sloe eyes against whom it would be a duty and a delight to pit one's wits. There were sudden swooping raids on the giant-stride, and the Greeks, who were cleverer than anyone else but torn by internecine strife, intrigued darkly behind the oleanders.

Everything was stultifying. Rising to my feet, I wandered off behind the bowling screens, muttering mutinously. Grown-ups were boringly playing cricket, still older grown-ups were more boringly watching them. Away behind the club house, on smooth lawns surrounded by poinsettias, inconceivably old and boring ones were playing croquet. The afternoon seemed interminable and down in the swings a full and various life was slipping by me.

Saturday was fortunately a race day. War or no war, the racing at Gezira went on as usual, and was perhaps the most English thing of all. There it all was, perfectly reproduced on an island in the Nile – the grandstand, the judge's box, the paddock, the red-faced starter, the white painted wooden rails around the course, the coloured silks of the jockeys, the restless rich international faces, pallid or swart; the shouting, the beautiful bored women, the regimental band under the tree playing selections from *The Gondoliers*. The only trifling discrepancy was a cobra underneath the Pari-Mutuel. Never quite pinned down, it occasionally evidenced itself by inflicting lethal injuries upon successful punters.

On race days the nannies and prams congregated under an enormous tree in the middle of the course. The shouting and the strains of the band came faintly; at the start of the race we rushed to the rails on the far side of the course – 'Don't go near the crowds, dear' – to applaud our favourite jockey who was called Digby. The jockeys swept by in a shouting swearing drove, they were mostly Egyptian, the pink face of Digby was conspicuous among them. The horses were smallish, part Arab. In between races there was the huge tree in which to play Mowgli and Bagheera; it was the perfect form of racing. I lay out Bagheerawise, along a swinging branch. Along to the left Frank Tottenham who hadn't really the figure for it, was being Kaa, the rock python. Peter Dudgeon, who had insisted on being Mowgli, had now bored of the project and was arranging some races. But races, I knew by experience, are never much good unless organized by grown-ups. There are too many arguments about whether people of six-and-a-half should start behind those barely six, and still more arguments about who has actually won. But Peter was an optimist. He and his sister Joan lived in a wildly interesting place on the edge of the desert that could only be approached by railway. Along this, one bowled in a trolley, with the bright dry air blowing in one's face. It was always a delectable expedition, and the Dudgeons, apart from their charm of character, had a mother who could be relied on not to produce tapioca pudding for lunch. Around their house at night hyenas made their gorgeously disagreeable noise, and they had a gardener recovering from a nervous disorder who could be seen watering acres of flower-pots out of an empty watering-can. What made the whole day entirely beautiful was that every so often, as we bowled through the palm groves, a train could be seen coming towards us along the single track. One had to jump off, briskly, and the trolley was lifted off the rails by the Egyptians who took it in turns to push it, and replaced it when the train had passed.

Away below the tree the nannies went on with their interminable knitting and talking. What could grown-ups find to talk about, all day and every day? My left leg hung loosely from the bough; it was, for the moment, the long black tail of Bagheera. Its end twitched lazily in the heat of the Indian noon. Along on his bough Frank Tottenham seemed so to have thrown himself into the part of Kaa as to have gone to sleep. Should we turn into the Bandar-log and start pelting the nannies with sticks and leaves? It hardly seemed worth it. Or one could switch to a man-eater, and make a long deadly drop upon them. But no, I was Bagheera, a dignified animal with a character to keep up. I moved my sable head slightly from side to side, taking care not to knock my whiskers on the twigs.

'She wants him to revive a dormant peerage,' Nanny Russell said.

'What's that, then?' Mary West asked, always a good feed for gossip.

'To revive a dormant peerage,' Nanny Russell impressively repeated.

My admiration for Tommy Russell increased. I saw him applying artificial respiration to a very old lord who looked rather like a dormouse and had fallen unconscious. He was surrounded by a posse of silent and respectful Egyptian police-men. Would the very old lord recover consciousness or wouldn't he? Mrs Russell, not unnaturally, was urging him on in this errand of mercy.

The afternoon wind, blowing over the berseem fields on the other side of the Nile from the desert beyond, stirred the branches of the tree, and the leaves clattered. Frank had stopped being Kaa and had woken up, and it seemed as if Peter Dudgeon was getting somewhere with his race meeting; we hastened to descend and participate. Although no runner, Frank was a game and co-operative character. Curly-haired and on the stout side, he existed as if permanently in a steam bath, but the warmth extended to his heart and he was the cause, during his brief life, of much cheer.

Alas it could not always be race day, and next week culmin-
ated in a trembling and terrible row. Deceiving Nanny into
supposing that I was going to play French cricket behind the
bowling screen I made away into the Swings. Hardly had I
enrolled myself in a very promising gang that was about to
make a foray upon the Copts and take away their tennis balls,
before Nanny appeared. Standing on the far side of the palings
she summoned me back and I refused to come. I shouted defiance at her and her face became suddenly crimson and
different. She could not, I knew, climb the palings, and by the
time she had gone round by the gate I could be off and away.

'I'm not coming! I'm not coming! Why don't *you* come in
the Swings instead? Why do you stay on the babyish old
cricket ground?'

'You're to come here to me. This minute. You're to come
out from there.'

Why must the people one loves *force* one into hurting
them? The look on Nanny's face, and the redness of it, ravaged
me. I loved her, and grieved for her upsetness; I hated her,
and fought for my freedom and grown-upness. After a brief
struggle between guilt and triumph, triumph won.

'I'm staying here.'

'You're a very naughty girl.'

Sticks and stones, I thought, may break my bones, but
words will never hurt me. I was not too sure about this, all the
same. I very much wanted Nanny to come right into the
Swings and settle there on her camp stool with her knitting so
that I could fall back upon her for protection when the pace

of life got too hot. I was eight, and people surely should accommodate themselves a bit to my plan of life? I wanted, as we all do, a safe base from which to conduct operations, but it had also to be a mobile base.

'Come along now. I'm waiting.'

'But WHY?'

'Because I say. I won't have you playing in there. Nasty rough games,' Nanny said, firmly closing her mind to the fact that I was a nasty rough child myself. 'And look at your clean dress already.'

'I'M NOT COMING!'

On the way home she hardly spoke, and I hit out dourly at the snake grass with my hoop stick, making, from time to time, ineffective attempts to suborn Alethea. At night I heard low voices on the landing; my mother was being told. The words 'unable to manage her' floated in, but they seemed to have no connection with me. A blanket of self-deception, deliberately imposed, hangs itself between act and consequence. A sentence, clearly heard, fails to register its import. I am afraid there is very little hope, the doctor says, and it seems to be the talk of a character in a book, having no relevance to us, to our situation. I had been naughty and Nanny had been cross. It would all soon be over as it always was. I slept sound, buoyed up with a sanguine obtuseness that could not be dignified by the grand name of hope.

XIII

In the spring of 1917 a kindly British Government came to the rescue of my nervous system by forbidding the transportation of women and children through the Mediterranean. This edict, although miserable for William who was thus obliged for nearly three years to spend his school holidays with relations who were unwaveringly kind and unwaveringly inadequate, was a piece of delightful luck for Alethea and me. It was also deliverance, for I still despaired of survival. Kitchener had been drowned in the previous autumn in the sinking of the cruiser *Hampshire* which had been taking him to Russia to shore up the crumbling Russians, and if the sea could swallow Kitchener what hope was there for me? But now, instead of voyaging to England, we were to spend the months at a summer camp on the northern curve of the Delta, called Brulos Beach.

This thought intrigued and excited us all through March, while the hamseen raged as usual, a hot choky sky-darkening wind from off the desert, full of sand and dust which silted in through the shut doors and windows, and a grilling April when Alethea and I pottered about the closed and shuttered house with our long hair done up in topknots for the sake of coolness. At evening the windows were opened and the sultry air swam in. Ahmed's successor, Suliman, threw buckets of water over the tiles of the verandah to cool it enough for bare feet to walk upon and beds were moved out there for the freshness of the night. Released from the house, we would rush out into the garden where already the flowers and grass were browning and dying in the scorching sun. The rabbits panted sadly in their hutches, eating less and less of their bran and berseem, and the breeze moving the sickle leaves of the eucalyptus trees seemed only to be distributing the dry heat around. By May the Nile seemed already perceptibly heightened, flowering trees flowered briefly and extravagantly, in the shady places the gardeners ceaselessly watered the plants in pots. Everything seemed to move more slowly; people, animals, even the trams; Egypt went about its business in a trance of baking heat. Across the Red Sea, in the scorching wastes of Arabia, Lawrence was mounting his campaign, and by the Canal the cavalry of Allenby was gathering for Cavalry's last brilliant battle, a form of warfare which, for Western Christendom at least, began and ended with the struggle against Islam.

We left for Brulos on an early morning in May. Access was by slow train through the Delta to the camp on the coast between Lake Burullos and the sea. We changed at Tanta, and again at Mehalla-el-Kebir on to a single line track, the Delta Light Railway, that swung importantly round rich alluvial fields and waited interminably at a great many small stations. Willows were dotted along the canal banks, and palms clustered round the villages, but otherwise the landscape was flat and empty. The white robes of the fellahin as they reaped the doura or followed the buffalo plough were dots against the open plain. This was haphazard indigenous country where the Egyptians came into their own. Even the engine driver was no longer a Scot. The Egyptian ticket collector moved casually along the outside of the train, laughing and chatting and spitting out chewed sugar cane and bullying enemies and accepting presents from friends who had omitted the formality of taking a ticket. There were prolonged altercations at every level crossing, while the heat sizzled on the carriage roof.

'We are not training enough of them,' my father said sadly. He had taken a few days' leave and come with us to see us settled in. 'The war has nipped all that in the bud. Every time a foreigner has to be given a job in the administration, because there isn't an Egyptian who knows how to do it, we should send one home to be trained to replace him. We don't look far enough ahead, just deal with day to day difficulties and shortages as they arise.'

'I suppose the war makes it all impossible?'

'What's Cambridge doing?' my father asked, who had been at Oxford himself. 'There can't be many undergraduates there and the dons must be mostly over military age. Why can't they train twenty or thirty young Egyptian scientists a year? To replace the hundreds of Cambridge scientists we employ over irrigation and cotton pests and so on?'

'But Will dear, how are they to get there in wartime?'

'That's true. They'd probably be torpedoed, and we'd never be forgiven. And the radical press would insist it was all a plot to drown any promising young Egyptians so as to maintain our hold on the country.'

It was very hot, and gloom settled on me. A terrible event had occurred that morning. Without any warning, without the elementary precaution of consulting Alethea and me, Nanny had left us, to look after a small girl called Susan Clay. The event had been, as far as possible, glossed over. 'I don't fancy, somehow, living in huts,' Nanny had said, and Susan Clay had been represented to us by my mother as being in far greater need of Nanny's skill and care than we were; a lonely delicate only child with far too thin a neck and no appetite. This picture failed to arouse the faintest glimmer of sympathy in my heart. Having partly precipitated the disaster, I was furiously indignant about it, and laboured under a grievous sense of wrong. If Nanny goes, I go too, Alethea had crisply said, revealing an unexpected Trade Union streak in her character. I must have blacklegged, because this threat had somehow been inoperative: the bosses had won.

'I sometimes think, all the same,' my mother said, 'that we could somehow do more for the poorest people, helping them, and the illiteracy?'

'If they'd adopt Roman letters for the everyday use of Arabic,' my father said, 'illiteracy would be no problem. After all we gave up Roman numerals several centuries ago because they were so cumbersome, and took to Arabic ones. They could swop their letters without loss of face. To read and write in Arabic letters requires a fairly high degree of intelligence, certainly more than the majority have. It would be interesting to know what the literacy figures in any country using Arabic characters now are.'

Why had my parents failed to consult Alethea and me over this fatal step? Why hadn't Nanny told us sooner, so that we could have put up more of a protest? We were too old, they said, for a Nanny. Really, what a decision! At Brulos, they said, where we would wear very few clothes and have Mary West to see to us, there would be nothing for Nanny to do. The whole thing seemed a lamentable error of judgement. I frowned furiously at the Delta and longed to have some way of biting it.

'As to helping the poorer people,' my father said, 'I know it's cried out for. All you can say is, that they were even worse off before we came. We have remedied the worst of the abuses, I sometimes think the only help one country can give another is technical. Roads and finance and hospitals and irrigation and education – yes. But to raise Egypt into the forefront of civilisation is for Egyptians themselves, and no one else.'

'I suppose so,' my mother said, not quite convinced.

'Cromer gave this country what it most vitally needed after the Khedival chaos, twenty years of benevolent and able despotism . . . Those days are done . . . plenty of Egyptians are politically conscious enough . . .'

Their voices went on. I was sleepy, cross, unable to sleep. The heat seemed to gather itself to strike, like a fist. The iced lemonade in the thermoses was all finished.

'. . . There are so many intelligent young Egyptians . . . Zaghlul.'

Nanny had left her address. She was presently going to

2,304 Vandux Avenue, Pasadena, California, U.S.A. It was estranging to think of more than two thousand homes in one long straight row, and Nanny inextricably among them, boiling milk and making jellies to tempt Susan Clay's appetite, and rubbing pommade divine into her bruises. We became much fonder of Nanny the minute after she had left, and continued to send her repellent knitted pen-wipers on March 17th, which was her birthday, for many years, as if these forlorn objects might exorcise our rudeness or neglect, might even bring her back. She continued to send us long letters in her curly writing, and birthday cards up to her dying day, which was in March, 1963, but things were never the same again, and children, as well as the old, strongly desire them so to be. One of the pillars of life had been removed, and I was prepared to extract the last ounce of grievance out of this situation, whenever I remembered to.

'. . . Other kinds of help somehow get patronising, interfering, cut across religion and custom and put backs up without knowing it. We can't be the Salvation Army to a whole people many of whom have a high grade civilisation of their own . . . plenty of able men like Mohammed Said or Hussein Roushdy, who aren't disposed to accept anything they don't agree with, have been running this country far more than anyone supposes . . .'

By two o'clock Alethea and I had begun to droop, and my father switched himself off Egypt and began to invent a long saga about a country called Bungaweel, inhabited by fabulous beasts called Catterwompuses which he drew for us on the back of O.H.E.M.S. envelopes. He did not mind the heat and was less generally preoccupied with climate than most grown-ups were. 'I shall be a pool of grease in a minute,' Nanny was for ever saying, on the walk back from school, and, 'Aren't you cold, darling?' my mother as frequently asked one, when in England. In point of fact one was never either too hot or too cold, except when bored; at other times climate simply never obtruded itself, seemed more to be a figment of the too fussy imagination of grown-ups. With so little of real moment to occupy themselves with, compared with children, they were obliged to invent and endlessly discuss imperceptible differences of temperature.

We arrived crumpled, tired, and late at Balteem where the railway ended, and had a meal with the two promoters of the camp in a sort of office before going on by launch down seven miles of canal to the sea. The luggage was decanted into a sailing felucca and proceeded downstream ahead of us. We chugged after it an hour or so later among banks of high bulrushes; it felt a long way. Suddenly, round a curve, came a stiff cool breeze, the end of the rushes, and the intoxicating smell of the sea-shore. There was a houseboat, moored alongside the canal bank, the long clapperboard building that contained the restaurant, and two rows of rush-matting huts stretching out along the coast to the westward.

'What are all those little sentry-boxes far out behind the huts?'

'Sentry-boxes, dear,' Mary West said. She could not possibly have told us what they were within earshot of the man at the wheel, a character who, as I had already discovered, spoke and understood only Portuguese and Arabic.

Attention was distracted by a merry crowd around the landing stage. Some were helpfully squeezing out our sodden cushions into the canal; others were seen to be energetically drying my mother's long evening dresses by running briskly about the sand with the dresses streaming out behind them like banners. All of our luggage was open and the contents were being wrung out by obliging spectators with fish-scaly hands, exclaiming delightedly at its quantity and quality, and calling upon God to witness their zeal and efficiency. The felucca, meeting the breeze at the mouth of the canal at a moment when its captain was preoccupied by an interesting discussion with a colleague, had capsized, fortunately without the slightest loss of life, and deposited all our luggage at the bottom of the canal which was happily not deep. Everything had been fished out, and the captain was proudly counting the tally. All was soaking wet and smelt of Nile. This had its sad side. Alethea's Tommy, a time-honoured individual in a pink smock, parted for ever from his plaster head, and the sawdust body of her Affa-Caffa developed an unfriendly lumpiness. She was obliged to fall back for comfort upon a white bear who seemed impervious to ducking and was called May Irene Hyacinth. The tins of ginger biscuits had all gone soggy. The pages of *Martin Rattler*, *The Daisy Chain*, *What Katy Did Next*, and *The Children of the New Forest*, were irretrievably stuck together; never now should we know exactly what Humphrey and Pablo did with that cart. But on the whole the picnic element triumphed. We slept, gloriously, in nothing, our Nilish nightgowns waving in the warm Mediterranean night. My father's white shirts had all taken the imprint of his blue or red library books, and looked far more interesting than they had before. We made our way between their wildly gesticulating arms, under the clothes lines, towards our sentry box. 'Use a shovel of sand, dear,' Mary West said, disapprovingly. She had prudently kept her own case beside her in the launch, having a firm Anglo-Saxon belief in the mismanagement practised by all orientals. She led us off to tea at the restaurant. Well-schooled by Nanny, she was carrying a tin of Lyle's Golden Syrup, in case the jam wasn't nice . . .

Delicious coolness blew from the sea, a lighthouse showed to the westward on a flat and distant point. From the river came the cheerful noise of the boatmen attempting to extract from my father a heavy payment for rescuing the luggage they had spilled, and the loud and equally cheerful voice of my father entering the argument quite as whole-heartedly. The sound of enjoyable expostulation floated down-river over the water. Jokes about seamanship and navigation would be made. Loud laughter would fill the air. There would be no doubt that he would come off best and that everyone would come off happy. But would we be allowed to bathe before we went to bed, now that there were no towels to dry us? Would they allow us to roll ourselves dry in the hot sand?

Brulos Beach was run by a Mr Tite and a Mr Wright, who, with their families, had immediately been nicknamed the

Mortally Tights and the Morally Rights. True to form, Mr Tite had built a billiard room and bar alongside the restaurant, in reply to which Mr Wright had whipped up a rush-matting chapel at the far end of the camp. Between these poles lay thirty or forty rush-matting huts. Ours was one of five rather grander square ones; it had wooden sides half-way up, and a beaten earth floor which my mother covered with Persian rugs as soon as they were dry enough. The beds were exceedingly hard and made of a sort of scaffolding of palm branches. Land crabs found their way in at nights and scuffled about underneath them, banging around vaguely among the palm branch scaffolding. This was compensated for by the fact that the moon also found its way in at night, splintering into brilliant rush-matting shaped strakes along the floor. There was a knot in the wooden wall by my bed; I pushed it out and thus had an interesting view of the world after bedtime. Two by two the grown-ups would sweep along the baked earth path to dinner in the restaurant, men in dinner jackets and women in floating evening dresses, their deep voices and their high laughter seemed to hang in the soft evening air, to leave an echo of itself long after they were gone. I often hoped to be still awake when they came out of dinner, but rarely succeeded. To see them pass was an endless fascination, the grown-up world that was somehow different and lighter-hearted after children were in bed. Free of the responsibility of parenthood they could go further back into being children themselves. Did parents feel a kind of relief when they only had each other to laugh at, to talk to? Perish the thought. All the same, there was something about them, walking down the path so gaily together. Mrs McLaughlin would float by with her silvery laugh and her stout freckled husband; she had red-gold hair and seemed always to be wearing a black dress. Then there were the handsome and romantic Goldsmiths, who were on their honeymoon, Canon Gairdner with his melancholy determined gait, and the charming ungainly features of Sir Kinahan Cornwallis. There were the Lasberrys, who were C.M.S. missionaries and angelicly good in a cheerful and relaxed manner, and Mrs Gairdner who seemed to make rather heavier weather of it. There were Captain Westropp, thin, dark, and silent, and Mrs Westropp, fair and happy and ebullient, and the Lewises, and the Gilbert Claytons; the Bolands, the Blunts and the Dudgeons, the Sharmans, the Wrights and the Tites, and the house-boat living Wylies, accompanied always by a large Airedale dog. Two by two they went by, living their mysterious grown-up lives; what could it be like to be one of them? They looked frivolous, even abandoned; sometimes in an uncontrolled and soppy manner they held each other's hands, the licentious things. This admirable hole in the wall cut two ways, however; and my boon companions were all too apt to tickle my ear with a feather during the siesta hour, startling me out of an enthralled session with *The Last of the Mohicans*.

Inland there were palm groves and vineyards, and pools locked over with hard salt which covered the scrub plants as with a hoar frost, and the immense shallow expanse of Lake Burullos. Between the coast and the cultivated land there were huge sand dunes anchored by reed barriers. Out of the sand grew beautiful white lilies, with stems that wept like daffodils. On these wide hard sands my father, first getting the permission of the local sheikh, organized the Wrights and the Tites into making a nine-hole golf course, the greens of watered sand rolled hard. Unaccountably, the white and red flags marking the greens were found to disappear as often as they were replaced. After this had gone on long enough to satisfy the flag hunger of all the little boys in this thinly populated area, my father went to visit the sheikh. He found him among his vineyards, a dignified and extremely upright figure, white-bearded and deliberate. There followed the usual prolonged and courteous interchange of comments upon the nature of God, which in Moslem countries replaces the English regulation two and a half minutes about the weather, before my father touched delicately upon the question of the flags. After a further three-quarters of an hour spent upon general topics of conversation the explanation very slowly emerged. 'We are all', the sheikh said, with his gravity becoming, if possible, deeper, 'worshippers of the One God.'

My father agreed that this was so.

'That is understood. And in virtue of this I allow in my neighbourhood the worship of Christ, upon whom be all blessings and peace. But that is all.'

That, my father agreed, was certainly all.

'But idolatry', the sheikh continued, fixing my father with a flashing Wahabi look, a searing Old Testament glance, 'I will *not* tolerate, neither today nor tomorrow, in these coasts.'

'Idolatry?'

'You have made as it were a number of threshing floors. And on these threshing floors an idolatrous worship is practised.'

Light began to dawn on my father, and he resolutely straightened his face.

'You yourself,' the sheikh said, 'I speak it with shame, are not blameless of this practice of idolatry. In the centre of the threshing floor men have set a red flag or a white flag, and approaching these flags with sticks in your hands you bow down before these flags and worship them.'

'No,' my father said.

'Therefore,' the sheikh continued inexorably, 'my people have destroyed these objects of your idolatry.'

It is to be doubted whether the sheikh was very much the wiser after my father had explained to him about golf. What surfeit of time and richness, what idle-mindedness, what unthinkably frivolous natures could persuade grown men to hit little white balls and walk long distances after them? A desert of incomprehension stretched between the patterns of their lives. But once my father had convinced the sheikh that the English were being childish rather than sacrilegious, they talked amicably together for a further half hour and the flags were left in peace.

On the shore fifty yards from our hut the tideless Mediterranean idly splashed and fell. At noon the sand was so hot that one had to fly over it at top speed, its heat penetrated even the horny skin on the soles of our permanently bare feet. We wore no shoes all summer, even the pleasures of worship were unmarred by the tightness of clean white socks, by the scratchiness of starched muslin dresses round the neck and under the arms. 'We praise Thee, Oh God,' I shouted delightedly in the rush-matting church, 'we acknowledge Thee to be the Lord.' The Te Deum was splendid, vision building, whether sung in the coolness of All Saints at Cairo, in the plunging saloon of the P. & O. ship in the Atlantic, on grey summer mornings in the mossy parish church at Sidmouth, or as here in the rush-matting hut with the sun splintering through the roof and the breeze blowing the candle flames on the altar at right angles to the candles. 'To Thee Cherubim and Seraphim continually do cry.' The cherubim sat on the cumulus clouds; their fat legs swung in the blue. Some had trumpets and some had drums, but all were having fun. They were naked and the sun shone on them and the breeze blew through their toes. 'To Thee Cherubim and Seraphim continually do cry: Holy, Holy, Holy, Lord God of Sabaoth, Heaven and earth are full of the majesty of Thy Glory.' If one pressed one's feet into the sand, it could be felt fountaining up between one's toes. Kneeling down, one's knees sank gratefully into the softness of it. 'Oh Almighty God, who alone canst order the unruly wills and affections of sinful men . . .' Sitting during the lesson, one could lift the sand up on to one's foot as if it were a spade and feel the sand pour off like water. 'To Thee Cherubim and Seraphim continually do cry.' Let others sing of prophets and martyrs; they were old, bearded, boring.

In a passion of enjoyment at both ends, I corkscrewed my feet down into the sand and lifted up my voice still more enjoyably and less tunefully. 'To Thee Cherubim and Seraphim continually do cry.' My mother leant over me and kindly pointed out that we had got to 'Vouchsafe, Oh Lord, to keep us this day without sin,' but like a stuck gramophone needle, I took no notice. 'To Thee Cherubim and Seraphim continually do cry Holy, Holy, Holy.'

Life flowed on in a swimming week after week of pleasure. One's brow, hot after running, was blown on by the sea wind; one's bum, chill after bathing, was consoled by the hotness of the sand. Plentiful food regularly comforted one's stomach. Born a blessed ten years too late, we had missed dying, in spirit or in fact, in the terrible trenches of France. But alas for poor William, far away at his cheerless prep-school, eating miserable rations and kicking miserable desks, away from the sun and the sea and the bright beams of parental love. It seemed the cruellest fate, and he replied to it by refusing to grow. I thought of him at first, sometimes, as we wandered far along the sandy coast collecting shells, or took picnics inland and slid down the high dunes and brought grapes and figs and dates from the sheikh and carried them home in the little rush baskets made by the sheikh's wife. I thought sometimes about the war, and sometimes about Nanny, but for the most part I ceased to think at all. 'We are having very gorgeous fun here,' my letters continued monotonously to inform my father. An endless procession of bright days flowed past, like the gold grains of the sand filtering through one's fingers, like the brilliant blue of the clear sea water circling one's legs and rising, rising into delicious coolness around the armpits, a breathless and invigorating slosh across the mouth. I lived in a mindless world, treading water. There was no longer any need to fear lions and tigers, no longer even any necessity to be one. Even my parents no longer seemed so essential; they were pleasing adjuncts, like the landscape, like the unimaginably splendid sunsets, the high up fronds of the palm trees rustling in the breeze of afternoon. I forgot Nanny, I forgot William, I forgot the war. I forgot wolves, and submarines, and the frightening middle parts of the sea. I lived in a dream of bliss, from which I occasionally emerged to win all the races. No one could stop me or overhaul me, and at the end of each triumphant race I leapt into a sort of sliding standstill in the sand, like a web-footed bird coming down on a lake.

The Holy Ghost had ceased to be a boy of fifteen blowing up balloons and had become more remote; perhaps he had telescoped himself into God the Father and God the Son. He had dispersed into the brilliant air, was somewhere dissolved into the sea, blown on the afternoon breezes, glowing in the bright returning days, and still with the tideless tranquillity of summer evenings along the mirror shore. He floated from me into an ungrasped and shadowy kingdom that was sometimes more real than the seen and concrete world. The jewelled railway platform of heaven had broken up, and showered down into the million pulses of sunlight on the sea. The Holy Ghost was a spirit and no more a body and I scarcely missed him. I was in love.

It is a wonderful thing at eight years old to be in love, when out of sight is truly out of mind. One embraces in an unrecognising manner the idea of love, the feeling of it in the air. In a blissful vacuum of ignorance, one loves without before or after, without suspense, regret, or hope. Some new kind of sun has arisen and shines through every unconsciously beguiling aspect of manhood. The loved objects, greatly enhancing life by their presence, are never given a second thought in their absence. They float in a pleasing undifferentiated haze. They could not be contemporaries; for who can love a little boy of eight in khaki shorts and a sun-helmet and front teeth too large for the rest? Probably only his mother: and even so, such soppiness is nigh inconceivable. Otherwise my requirements were simple, and I was in love at Brulos with about ten per cent of the male personnel. They had to be at least as old as fifteen, and under twenty five, for after that of course decrepitude sets in. I was in love with a young married man called Oliver something, I was in love with the curate, with a wounded soldier on leave, with the man who worked the motor-launch and spoke only Portuguese with a few words of Arabic, with one of the young waiters, with the junior lighthouse keeper, and with a blue-eyed fisherman who cast his net at the mouth of the canal.

'He's a German spy, of course,' Bunny Tite said, 'or why has he got blue eyes?'

'He's a Turkish spy,' Frank Tottenham said, 'you wouldn't get a German knowing how to cast a net like that. Even my father can't.'

'Whoever heard of a Turk with blue eyes?' Bunny scornfully asked.

'Circassian Turks have blue eyes,' Frank knowledgeably told him. 'I bet a million pounds he's a Turkish spy. We'd better keep a good watch on him.'

I was pleased to comply with this plan, though I felt pretty sure they were wrong. No one with so charming a face could possibly be on the wrong side. The loved objects all lived ideal lives and could not harbour a harsh thought. How could Bunny and Frank know? Boys of seven and eight, their judgements must be valueless. Their eyes were tight shut and they were quite incapable of entering into the dream. Love at eight years old is an uncomplicated and dreamy pleasure, like religion; whose joys it overlaps. It is like a box of chocolates, or a good book, or catching a fish in the canal; like an omelette or a sunset or the finding of a rare large shell, a pleasure unblemished by pain, jealousy or disappointment; sensations which are confined to the concrete realities of life, such as the prize for the flat race or who has the first turn from the diving board. Gosh, one thought, here comes Oliver, gosh, golly, gonkin! His hair turned up at the ends in a way that was curiously affecting. Quite unaware of what had got into one, in no way did one connect it with the soppy goings-on of grownups. How gorgeous, it's fruit salad, handed round by Hussein, his teeth gleaming white in a regular-featured face that was exactly the colour of one's bronze dancing shoes. Gosh, golly! Emotion did not prevent one taking the largest possible helping. None of the redundant adult emotions have elbowed their way in, and love is an unadulterated joy. One sleeps, if possible, even better at nights.

We used to go out in the very early morning to see the fishermen casting their nets at the mouth of the canal. My loved object, a figure even more interesting than the general run of fishermen, had a fringe beard, and he and his brother were in dress, looks and occupation, exactly like James and John the sons of Zebedee in Hole's *Illustrated Gospel*. The fishermen stood on the river bank, or knee-deep among the shoals of the sea, with their loins girt up and their gala-biahs rolled into their belts. Gathering their nets together they cast them out over the deep water with a sudden dexterous fling of the arm. The circle of the net slowly sank, was drawn in, sometimes a fish flashed its white belly in the breathless light. The sand, cooled by a night's freedom from the sun, moved refreshingly underfoot. We gathered close to look into the nets. Sometimes we took cigarettes and exchanged them for the fish. Again and again the nets swirled and sank, splashless in the extravagant blue of the sea. Waves scarcely fell, the waters of the canal lay mirror-still, and white against the orient light of early morning. The footmarks in the sand were pools of blue. To the east the palm groves stirred their feathers faintly. There is an untarnished sharpness of delight with which the heart in childhood receives its impressions. The scene was painted in colours of unimaginable clarity, was bathed in still and timeless light. There was no movement but the bending of the fishermen's backs, the silent splash of their spread nets falling in the water. At any moment Christ Himself would come out from amongst the palm groves and walk along that silent shore to tell them, 'Follow me, and I will make you fishers of men.'

XIV

"'Confidence in himself and his fortunes returned with his reviving spirits, and with the rising sun. He thought of his love no longer as a desperate and fantastic dream, but as a high and invigorating principle, to be cherished in his bosom although he might never propose to himself, with all the difficulties by which he was beset, to bring it to any prosperous issue. The pilot", he reflected, "steers his bark by the polar star, although he never expects to become possessor of it."'

It was the autumn of 1917. I sat with my father in the large armchair in the corner of the drawing-room nearest the verandah. Its springs had never been the same since my Alleluia days, but it was wide and it comfortably held two people and it was close to the cool air of the evening. The sun was preparing itself to set in its usual blaze of glory, and the entire western sky, seen through the eucalyptus trees, was orange-coloured. Our faces shone orange-coloured in the furnace of light. I was about to be nine years old, and kept impressing this interesting fact upon my father, who was reading *Quentin Durward* to me.

'I shall never', I persisted, 'be eight again. All that is over.'
'. . . "and the thoughts of Isabelle of Croye shall make me a worthy man-at-arms," my father read on, undeterred.

'Do you realize, Father, I never again will be eight, after this evening?'

'No. You won't. – "though I may never see her more. When she hears that a Scottish soldier, named Quentin Durward, distinguished himself in a well-fought field."'

'Nine is almost double figures. Nine is a cube or something.'

Like most women I adored talking about myself before an appreciative audience, and like most men, my father could take just so much and no more. He urged me to shut up and let him get on with the story, but I was riveted in a concern with the mystery of age, the strange unstoppable passage of time. Finally he gave up and suggested we should go for a walk before it got too dark.

At the piano my mother was playing and singing to Alethea, who was musical, but my slight musical appetite had been effectively dulled by lessons with Miss Simpson and I hated the piano, and would only listen for extremely short stretches even to my mother's playing. So that I very often went for walks alone with my father across the river and among the fields on the other side. Here the sugar cane and the doura stood as tall as a coppice, thick mysterious forests of rich growth. There were fields of berseem, and often a kingfisher to be seen along the banks of the larger canals. White egrets stepped delicately about in the muddy channels which ran between every field. This was the plain where Napoleon's army defeated the Mameloukes and where he made that remark about forty centuries looking down upon them, which the French think so full of *gloire* and the English think so showing-off. There cannot, in Napoleon's time, have been quite so many canals, or the battle would have been one long water-jump. The Mameloukes had been encamped at Embaba the night before their defeat, and anyone, but especially Nanny, could have told them that no good would come of that.

Living in this country at this time, brought up upon these evening walks, I am unable to believe that colonialism is at all times and in all places an evil thing. It is possible to fool an eight- or nine-year-old child about a great many things, but not about overt expressions of love or hate, and what the Egyptian countrymen overtly expressed at this time was love and friendship. Many of them were old enough to remember the miseries perpetuated by the rule of their own countrymen under the nominal suzerainty of Turkey, and they very much preferred ours; whether we were white, black, beige, yellow, paternal, fraternal, or just rather too lazy, preoccupied, and uninterfering. The older fellahin could remember the kourbash and the corvée, forced labour called upon at the sound of a whistle, and twenty lashes on the soles of the feet for whoever arrived last, and they appreciated justice, mercy, and order, and the men who administered it, wherever they hailed from. It was, of course, a honeymoon that could not last, a marriage that the war was already breaking up. There was shouting from the students of the university of Al Azhar, the oldest university in the world and steeped in Islamic pride. There were rumblings from the Delta, where all the younger administrative British had gone away to fight in the war, to be replaced not by Egyptians, because no one had time to train them, but by other British who were older and more prejudiced and spoke no Arabic and had no knowledge of the country. The recruiting by the hard-pressed British Army of the Labour Corps, Egyptians more or less press-ganged from their homes in the provinces by local mudirs on the paying-off-old-scores principle, had aroused great bitterness. So that under the pressure of war and the requisitioning of farm animals and cotton crops, when compensation paid to the farmers was long delayed and sometimes went into the wrong pockets *en route*, discontent was building up. The war in Palestine, now that the immediate menace of the Turks was removed to a safe distance, could be felt to be in some sense Christendom *v.* Islam, the bustling and materialist west against the slow and holy east, and little as they wanted the Turks back, who had lorded it over them for so many centuries, there was no doubt where the religious feeling of the Egyptians lay.

'If only', my father said, walking in front of me along the narrow path by the canal, 'they could have a real ruler of their own. Someone of world stature, bred on the banks of the Nile. It's too long since there's been one. Cleopatra was a Greek, descended from one of Alexander the Great's generals, Saladin was a Kurd, Mohammed Ali was an Albanian Turk.'

'What about the Sultan?'

'Well,' my father said, 'Fuad is a very pleasant and in some ways a wise man, but not just one to set the Nile on fire.'

The sunset, now, was doing exactly this to the canals, and the line of the desert hills was dark blue. From the fields an old man who was still working called down a blessing on us as we passed, and my father's voice answering him, seemed suspended in the stillness of the air. The kingfishers had all gone, it was beginning to be dark. From the fields a heavy warm smell rose into the coolness of the night, a lush, fertile, river-mud smell. One could almost feel the crops growing in the extraordinary richness of the dark earth; El Khemi, the soil of Egypt whose magic fertility had produced the word alchemy. The lights of Em-baba shone dimly across the flatness of the landscape; behind a screen of palm trees a golden tram was grinding slowly over the Zamalek bridge; the brilliant stars pricked out. We walked now hand-in-hand, discussing the independence of Egypt. It was to be a country solvent, secure, and free; with the fellahin earning a living wage for their unending labour, with no more bullying of the poor, with everyone equal before the law, no more selfish exploitation in the midst of misery. It was a dream to which he had cheerfully dedicated his life; more, in a characteristically English way, by accident than design. For a few moments, on this black warm evening, I forgot about being nine tomorrow and shared it with him. He had a giving nature, and he thought we had plenty to give the Egyptians. Without self-righteousness, and without even much self-consciousness, he was a missionary for good government, regarding it as the beginning of the relief of misery. He and many like him were in some ways as selfless in their task as a missionary could be. It is true that they enjoyed the good things of Egypt, the winter climate and the cheerful willing servants and the lush perennial gardens and the splendours of the antiquities, but they also employed their excellent brains, not in self-enrichment, not in safety, not in comfort; but enduring long separations from home and family, a summer climate often lethal, strange diseases, strange foods, and the certainty of straitened means at the end of it all, retirement on a small pension and probable ill-health. They had also the virtual certainty that everything they had done would be roundly abused at the receiving end.

Permanent domination by one race over another was a notion foreign to their way of thought. Aware of having been taught by the Romans not to paint themselves blue, it would have seemed to them the height of bad manners not to pass on the good news. The process, as all knew, was disagreeable at the time to those at the receiving end: naturally one fought against it. This was a reaction taken for granted by the colonisers: they did not expect or court popularity. Knowing what was then known in England about administration, medicine, irrigation, and the scientific control of agricultural pests, could men of education and goodwill be so selfish and irresponsible as not to colonize? With all that barbarism and defeatism around, could the good man simply sit at home making money? To do so was, as it were, a failure to pay one's U.N.O subscription. They thought of their colonial jobs as V.S.O. or the Peace Corps might now think of theirs; as interesting, dangerous, ungainful, and very much in the general interest. Often humble about themselves, they were very unhumble about the quality of the goods they purveyed, firmly convinced that equal justice and uncorrupt administration were foundations without which no good life could be built. It was an exercise in love and duty and like so many such it fell flat on its face because too many practitioners had not enough imagination and made it offensive to too much *amour propre.* Or did it? Time will show.

Characters like my father were not much vexed by the short-term reactions of some of the governed, because they had themselves all been brought up on Milton and on 'as He pronounces lastly on each deed, Of so much fame in Heaven expect thy meed', and on *Magna est veritas et praevalebit,* all of which supplied them with impetus and took them through the frequently disagreeable and frustrating aspects of their task. It was an attitude dangerously veering towards smugness. A necessary balance against the hubristic nature of their calling was preserved because they all, every night, as regularly and thoroughly as they cleaned their teeth, knelt and besought God to forgive their shortcomings. Without this they would far more rapidly have become insufferable. The weakness of colonialism is the invariable element amongst the colonizers that goes bad in the heat.

'The population has gone up to thirteen million', my father said, 'in the forty years since we've been here, from the five or six million it had been steadily for centuries. We have doubled the acreage under the plough. They never really controlled the Nile, and thousands starved every so often, apart from cholera and other plagues. Now, perhaps among all those extra saved children a great man is growing up. It's in the nature of things that one of them should.' And in the nature of things that one of them should be Gamal Abdel Nasser.

We had gone far, I was tired by the time we got to the bridge. The night was very dark, star-lit; in the darkness you could smell the scent of the flowers in the garden wafting over the hedge, jasmine and rose, and the tobacco plant whose white flowers showed through the darkness. The eucalyptus trees rustled pungently at us as we passed. There were more stars than ever, but my sandals were full of dust. Supposing one's parents, somehow, actually *forgot* one's birthday? What if one came along in the morning and there were no parcels by their bed, and one's mother just said, 'Oh darling, your birthday, is it really? I'd quite forgotten. How extraordinary, the whole thing had quite gone out of my head!' Could such a nightmare as this really occur? What if one's father were still preoccupied with Roushdy Pasha?

Life this winter was more fun than ever. The war, now that it no longer seemed likely to hurt *me*, was interesting rather than menacing, and the constant presence of a great number of soldiers was nearly as much appreciated by me as it was by Mary West. Christmas was as gay as ever, or gayer; the parties more flowing, the Christmas stockings more bulging, the presents more surprising, the Turkish Delight more sticky and nutty (though surely less Turkish). McMahon, who came to be known as the pink pearl, had been relieved at the Residency by Sir Reginald Wingate, a small active figure who had been Sirdar of the Sudan. His wife was called Kitty, like the love-lorn rhinoceros at the Giza Zoo, insisted on choosing the hymns for matins as often as Mr Horan would let her, and was a dab hand at controlling the A.D.C.s, who had often in Cairo shown a complicating inclination to involve themselves with the beautiful wives of influential Syrians. The Wingates had a superbly huge Christmas tree in the Residency ballroom to which everybody came; the Goschens all wore Lincoln green and moved about in a small compact body like Robin Hood and his Merry Men. In January Alethea and I were surprised and disconcerted to be asked to accompany our mother to lunch with Lady Wingate. It made the day feel like Sunday, and involved the putting on of white socks in the morning. There were courgettes for lunch, my unfavourite vegetable. The shade of Nanny stood firmly behind me, urging me to finish up everything on my plate because of all the poor children who would be thankful for it. There was no very obvious method, in that large dining-room, with so many suffragis waiting on us, for disposing of the unwanted courgettes. If this was grown-up life, they were welcome to it. The A.D.C.s, subdued by Lady Wingate, were less jolly than might have been hoped, and anyway, as it was wartime, they were all characters with one lung, or one kidney, or one leg, or some other dispiriting liability. After lunch, Lady Wingate, having got us there, seemed at a loss what next to do with us. Finally she sent us into the Residency garden to kick a large brand-new football about. Perhaps she had confused us with someone else and expected us to be boys. Happy as I was to spend long mindless hours throwing a tennis ball against a wall and catching it again, the football was too much. To kick a football about Alethea and I resolutely refused as soon as Lady Wingate had gone back into the house. Of all the boring boys' occupations! We had to be content with dropping gravel over the wall into the Nile, avoiding, as far as possible, the company of the adjutant bird that always lived there. It was not that we had anything personal against it; it was just deeply unsympathetic, and I have always wished that adjutant birds had never been thought of, although no doubt in their natural habitat they serve some useful end. The sun blazed on the grass which, re-sown every year, was of a billiard-table green. An A.D.C., despatched to see how we were getting on, told us that the grass seed for the lawn cost a hundred and fifty pounds a year, a piece of entirely uninteresting information which has remained with me for ever and which I sometimes still find myself using as a yardstick. Later on Lady Wingate seemed to repent the error that had arisen over the football, and gave us each some embroidery scissors with which we were perfectly delighted.

One morning in February of this winter, standing under the bohinnia trees which were just coming into flower, my mind underwent one of those unaccountable changes of gear by which the process of growing up is sometimes suddenly accelerated. I was holding in my hand one of the hard seed pods of last year's bohinnia flowers, like a curved piece of wood-carving, beautiful, exact and true; and rough like the shell of a Brazil nut. My spirit took a leap forward which startled the flesh it inhabited. Everything seemed all at once more real, more exciting, more beautiful, and more involved in me. I looked back upon yesterday's self and was unable to imagine how it could possibly have been so stupid, so babyish, or so fast asleep. I felt as a snake must feel, rolling out of an old skin. Who could this have been, a character afraid of wolves and unaware of the softness of mimosa, its yellowness, its unique smell and way of growing? Surely not me. I stretched my legs and they went faster, I climbed a tree and I went higher. This may well be the less disagreeable side of dying. The only concrete and immediate result of this soul's awakening was that I wrote a series of poems about the freesias and bignonias and sunsets of such revolting sentimentality that even my kindly parents were bereft of comment. I was put on to a course of Parish's Chemical Food, red water full of iron and tasting not unpleasant, there being a general feeling that I must have outgrown my strength.

XV

The second summer at Brulos Beach was less dreamy, more eventful, than the first. The English passion for activity, that accompanies them through no matter what climate, was given full rein. Perhaps a general parental feeling had crept in that Satan would find some mischief still for idle hands to do; anyway there was more organisation. Sports every Saturday, sand-castle competitions, handicraft exhibitions, a general encouragement to Do and not to Dream. Morning lessons set in, in a small room behind the billiard-room, though not, alas, with Miss Quibell. Perhaps Miss Quibell felt happier to preserve her mystique by remaining in the large cool museum among the Pharaohs in Cairo and not risking the relaxed bathing-dress atmosphere of Brulos. Church this summer was unexpectedly around the billiard table; perhaps the rush-matting chapel with its guttering candles had burnt down. Here at morning Sunday School we were organised by charming Mrs Lasbery into marching round the billiard table singing hymns, which was splendidly active, and enjoyed by all, as long as the hymn was 'Bright the vision that delighted', or 'The Son of God goes forth to war, A kingly crown to gain', or 'Onward Christian Soldiers, marching as to war'. 'Soldiers of Christ, Arise', we shouted; our bare feet thumped pleasurably on the boards in a manner that might have surprised John Milton. Feeling perhaps that the whole thing was becoming a bit off-key and martial, the authorities confronted us next Sunday with a new hymn on a different note.

'Praise Him, Praise Him,' we sang doubtfully, 'all ye little children, He is Love, He is Love.'

Mrs Lasbery, kind and sweet as ever, urged us on, but this hymn is a lurid example of the sort of thing that the adult world erroneously supposes that children will be able to stomach, being too sweet and innocent to know better. I noticed with horrified delight that my partner in the march, Peter Dudgeon, was loudly singing, 'Praise Him, Praise Him, all ye little donkeys'. Thus introduced to the pleasures of blasphemy, I longed, but did not quite dare, to join in. 'Love Him, Love Him, all ye little brickbats,' Peter continued in the next verse, 'He is Love, He is Love.' Eleanor Gairdner from behind tapped him on the shoulder, but he continued unmoved. 'Serve Him, Serve Him, all ye little soapsuds,' Peter carolled. I listened, entranced, to see where the flight of his fancy would carry him next. His face was radiant with enjoyment, his feet beat out the rhythm, no fire from Heaven descended to consume him, 'Crown Him, Crown Him, all ye little wigwams,' Peter sang on. This was too much for me, and I was told sternly to go outside until I could stop laughing.

The Te Deum still held its undisputed grip upon my soul; not even Peter Dudgeon could or would take the mickey out of that. 'To Thee Cherubim and Seraphim continually do cry,' I shouted, slightly more in tune than last summer, on Sunday mornings across the green stretches of the billiard table. 'Heaven and earth are filled with the majesty of Thy glory. To Thee Cherubim and Seraphim continually, continually, CONTINUALLY do cry.' It was the same idea, only how much less soppily expressed.

Absent from these sessions in the billiard room were the McLaughlin family. Questioned about this, they admitted, blushing deeply all over that small portion of their faces that was not covered in freckles, to being Roman Catholics. It was clearly a source of dreadful embarrassment to them, to be different in such an important particular from all other children, and I was not so unkind as to pursue so shameful a topic. Applied to, my mother firmly but undisparagingly said that Roman Catholics were people who liked their church services in Latin, and were generally Irish, French, or Italian. No one truly English, I gathered, although these words were not spoken, could be so paltry as not to belong to the Church of England. Other races, of course, one must not judge. The McLaughlins, she said, were Irish, and they were, as I could see for myself, extremely nice people. She had a way of neatly tying up a subject and as it were putting it away in a drawer, not wishing to excite enmity. In no place are religious fightings between Christians more distressful than in the middle east, where Roman Catholic and Eastern Orthodox priests, quarrelling over right of way in procession, draw blood from each other with their crucifixes and are separated by Moslem policemen with a weary tolerance born of long experience.

The noons shone hot and splendidly. From eleven o'clock

onwards everyone was in the sea. My hair went yellow again, as in babyhood; Alethea's face shone brown and brilliant in the sun. We wore cotton bathing dresses and our heads were tied up for the sea in spotted handkerchiefs. This was an age when women over their youth were well-covered over for the sea; some of them even wore stockings. My mother had a belted full-skirted tunic over sort of moderated plus-four knee-breeches, it had short sleeves and a square neck-line. The total effect was rather like the uniform of a Persian satrap at the time of Darius, and very dignified and charming. Sometimes dolphins came inshore and leapt about amongst us, and when my father was there I swam with him across deep water to the second sandbank. Sometimes the dolphins appeared between us and the shore, and then they seemed a little disconcerting and rather too large. After lunch silence fell over the camp and everyone went to sleep, all except my mother, who drew no comfort from a siesta, and remained upright, doing embroidery or writing letters to her brothers and sisters. Painfully and slowly, I was learning my catechism by heart; my Duty to my Neighbour is inseparably connected with the afternoon breeze over the hot sand, with the feeling of my heels pushing against the planking of the hut wall as I lay on my palm-branch bed. My duty to my neighbour is to love him as myself and to do unto all men as I would they should do unto me. Round about three o'clock the splashing of the waves always became a little bit louder as the breeze freshened. To love, honour, and succour my father and mother. To honour and obey the King, and all that are put in authority under him. What sort of jam for tea, I wonder? Chicken and ham paste, with luck. To submit myself to all my governors, teachers, spiritual pastors and masters. (But not Miss Simpson, or, come to that, Mademoiselle Matthéi.) To order myself lowly and reverently to all my betters. (Like Mr Horan, and one's grandparents.) To hurt nobody by word or deed. If I could finish this there might be time before tea to play round the children's golf course with the little mashies that my father had had made for Alethea and me in Cairo. To bear no malice nor hatred in my heart. To bear, to bear – oh goodness what comes next? Frank Tottenham can learn by heart quite easily. But he can't swim out as far as the second sandbank. To be true and just in all my dealings. But that ought to have come in before. Not to covet nor desire other men's goods, but to learn and labour truly to get mine own living. I've left out about keeping my tongue from evil-speaking, lying and slandering, and my body in temperance, soberness and chastity. Temperance means not being greedy, soberness means not getting in a fuss, chastity means not showing off. If I begin at the beginning again perhaps it will go better. *Martin Rattler* was lying at the foot of the bed and I opened the first chapter with my toes. If only one could read a book with one's toes and learn by heart with one's heart at the same time. Learning by heart was stone-breaking labour. I finally dissolved into tears over my inability to master an outward and visible sign of an inward and spiritual grace, although it had a sort of rhyme to it.

In any large collection of adults there will always be a generous person prepared to put themselves about on behalf of other people's children. Such a one was Mr Boland, who would read aloud in the shade of his hut after lunch every day for half an hour to an assembled company of children. He read us *Poor Jack, In the Eastern Seas,* and *Masterman Ready,* which proved to be too exciting for Dicky Cornwallis and Harley Archer who were only three and had to be withdrawn from the sessions. He read extremely well; everyone sat very still, hardly even playing with the sand. The large gentle eyes of Janey Clayton seemed to grow larger and rounder every minute. Sometimes he was unable to resist a tease. The sentence, '"Merciful Heavens," exclaimed Mrs Segrave, "what a deliverance!"' is one which occurs frequently in the narrative of *Masterman Ready.* Mr Boland's game was to introduce it into the text rather more often than it occurred to see whether he could get away with it. He was charming and funny and we deplored his return to his task at the Sudan Office in Cairo.

Lurking always in the undergrowth of the mind, again this summer the Joneses reared their hoar ubiquitous heads. Perhaps the Saturday afternoon sports startled them from cover. A raging desire to excel laid hold upon the spirit and gave it only intermittent rest. It was fun that too readily became serious, bit one in the innards. I could win the races, except for the potato race for which I lacked the necessary guile and quick-wittedness, but somehow this Saturday triumph never lasted far into the week. By Tuesday the Joneses were out in force once more. Other people, threateningly, could do other things much better. Alethea was small enough to ride my father in the blindfold fathers' race. Judy

McLaughlin could stay longer under water. Stella Lasbery was prettier, and her hair was fairer. Boys were still more serious rivals. Only intermittently did I wish to be one; it became more important to be even with them. One seemed at this point in life to have insufficient weapons against them. Superior speed was not all. Boys were stronger, more persistent, higher climbers, deeper divers. They gloried in and out of season in these feats. Sometimes it seemed that all one could do about them was to laugh at them; even then they were capable of turning the tables. Their technical resources seemed unlimited; they could, like Peter Dudgeon, knock off a model steam-roller out of old tin cans. Why were girls' manufactures of so much less account? I myself, coached by Mary West, whose leisure moments were entirely spent in making crochet tops for nightdresses, had made a crochet pin-cushion cover. It had taken me a long while, and there were no mistakes in it, but even my mother, who received it with the words 'Very elegant', had a note of discernible mockery in her voice. Far different was the reception accorded by her to a collection of assorted shells in matchboxes, garnered together in an old chocolate box upholstered painstakingly in green flowered linen. But even this, my *chef d'oeuvre*, was as nothing in the handicrafts competition compared with Peter's steamroller, which won first prize, and around which the grown-ups clustered in an admiring bunch. Joan Dudgeon had assured us beforehand that it would be something remarkable, and she had been right.

Then there was Paddy, a curly-haired boy who fished all

day by the canal in a rapt and timeless silence. I fished myself, from time to time, with a palm branch and a bent pin, handicapped by a stony dislike of baiting the pin with a mussel, but I knew myself incapable of this speechless day-long dedication, into which even hunger seemed unable to penetrate. With difficulty was he borne away from the canal bank by his disobliging parents to swallow a modicum of food. Where did boys acquire this eerie detachment from the human race? When it came to acting, it was the same old story. Amusing character parts, like the March Hare and the Mad Hatter, went to boys. It was true that Rettles de Cosson was the dormouse which was at least a part with something in it to bite on, but most of it was sleep. Why did I have to wear a frilly apron and be that tame Alice? Joan and Peter Dudgeon, looking unfairly handsome, were allowed and indeed encouraged to do a song and dance turn that their mother had taught them, about a soldier doll and his wife, full of spirit and activity. Dourly I carried on with my task of addressing a grin without a cat, and afterwards, behind the billiard-room, took off the apron and jumped it down into the sand. The Alice books were too surrealist and far out for me, though my mother could never read the court scene in *Through the Looking Glass* without tears of laughter running down her face.

'Douglas', Eleanor Gairdner said, 'is already well into fractions.'

He was two years younger, a mere seven, and I had only just begun fractions myself. Like Goering when he heard the word culture, I reached for my revolver. I wanted very much to roll Douglas Gairdner over in the sand and get it in his mouth. Perhaps he would do something mean to Alethea, which would justify the onslaught. But Douglas Gairdner was a boy without vice. He continued to stand there, in the dry sand, flaxen-haired, with a slightly open mouth, wearing his mathematical superiority like a smart new sun-hat.

'I'll fight you', I said feebly, 'with one hand behind my back.' I had heard Paddy say this and it sounded all right, but which hand did honour demand?

'Douglas', Eleanor said, 'doesn't care for fighting. He thinks it's pointless.' What, then, could one do about the fractions? 'I'll give you ten yards start and race you –'

'We are building', Eleanor said in a definite and civilized voice, 'a cathedral for the sand competition.' And there it stood in its churchyard, tall and smooth and late gothic, with seaweed for grass and dried white cuttlefish for tombstones. Canon Gairdner, carefully not helping, sat close by and issued minute instructions. He had rimless glasses and neat dark blue shorts. 'The tower', he said, 'must be three-quarters as high as the nave.' Fractions again! Bother and drat it! I had myself embarked upon a construction of Front-de-Boeuf's castle out of *Ivanhoe* and it was refusing to come right. Alethea, bored by my tyranny, had wandered away to join the Westropp twins, and Judy had been summoned away by her mother. I stood grudgily among the battlements, a sad and lagging Jones. There was no tide, and the cathedral seemed likely to remain there indefinitely, winning first prize and lording it for days over the calm Islamic landscape of the shore.

Lessons in the mornings seemed stodgy and unnecessary. Early though it was, the sun beat down upon the wooden walls of the billiard-room. Exercise books of squared paper lay open on the table; one's hands stuck to the paper. Why should I divide 7 million, 5 hundred and 23 thousand, 8 hundred and ninety-one, by 373? What is the point of long division? None; I decided in a sudden burst of glorious rationality, truly none. This was one of the few sensible rebellions of my childhood; life has never called upon me to long divide. I might have been learning Arabic or Greek or Italian, or some other useful and illuminating thing of that kind. The rebellion was dramatic and satisfactory, at least at the moment of its inception. I threw my book on the ground, overturned my chair and jumped out of the window. Only twelve feet, and a soft sand landing, but affording a wild pleasure all the same. I hurried home, breathless and defiant and spoiling for a further dust-up. There was a grand picnic to Lake Burullos scheduled for the afternoon; I made sure I should be forbidden to go. My mother was sewing when I arrived.

'Oh really darling, how silly to run away! But since you are here perhaps you'd be so kind as to fetch me my scissors from the dressing-table in my room.'

'But am I going to the picnic?'

'Well of course; why ever not?'

This clemency was disconcerting. I had settled my mind to a solitary afternoon, nursing dark thoughts beside the sounding sea, and now my mother was behaving as though virtually nothing had occurred; the chance of a pleasurable martyrdom was being whisked from under my feet.

'Why don't you get on with your hem?' my mother asked. 'There's time before lunch.'

Mohammed had recently taken a new young wife and had twins, a boy and a girl, and Alethea and I were making them pink cotton dresses. I sought refuge, bewildered, in a little occupational therapy. The dark thoughts, finding nowhere to settle, buzzed rather crossly off my mind. For a moment I took the weight off my legs and leant upon my mother's glorious restful imperviousness; the certain knowledge that one's captiousness and folly splashed themselves in vain against the rock of her love, and of her calm faith that one would turn out all right in the end. I went, a deflated balloon, to the picnic; and continued the long division on Monday morning at the point where I had left off. I lacked the stamina for a real revolutionary.

Lake Burullos was wonderful. One sailed with the fishermen in feluccas, out and out and out into the middle, far out of sight of the low-lying land. The fishermen spread a great circular net from boat to boat, and then, springing into the lake, revealed that the water was still only waist-deep. Fish leapt and gleamed in the hot evening sunshine, all was shouting, arguing, laughter, and great churnings up of masses of alluvial mud; for here the Nile, like the shorn and parcelled Oxus, disperses itself by lakes and many channels to the sea. My heart, released from long division, leapt and glittered with the fish. Mud, and wet net, and fish smells, and Egyptian food smells, filled the air; the feluccas lurched under the weight of fishermen climbing back on board again. Tea was spread out ashore in a scrub that looked like dried and burnt out heather, between shallows of solid salt like frozen pools. How blue the curate's eyes were, how thin and beautiful his legs! There were buttered scones and sardine sandwiches and plum cake, an English picnic tea. Less English were the baskets of grapes and figs – 'Have they been *washed,* dear?' 'In permanganate?' 'Oh yes, Mrs Lewin saw to it herself.'

Nursery routine obtained even here; bread and butter first, more amusing things later. Now they were handing round the basket of figs; there was one very big one, would it still be there when the basket came to me? This preoccupation absorbed my entire being. Michael Lewin, who was only four and knew no better, had missed it, so had Mrs Lewin and Katherine Wright; would it get to me, would it, would it? Oh, the boringness of manners; why cannot one just walk across the circle of munching laughing picnickers and get there first and TAKE the biggest fig? Now it is only three people away from me. Bunny Tite has got it. Whang, bang, whoosh, to Bunny Tite. But only, alas, in the imagination of the heart. The chains of civilisation hung heavy on me, gloomy great unnecessary things. But look, underneath the big fig there is a still bigger one! If one could discreetly get it out without stirring up the other figs, as in spillikins, it was all right, allowable, would pass for manners with all except such eagle-eyed observers as Nanny had been. It is out. It is mine. Its luscious red inside rolled round my mouth. It's bigger, even, than the one Bunny Tite got. Sucks, sucks, sucks to Bunny Tite.

We rode home on donkeys through the sandhills and the vineyards, singing as we went. The grown-ups, in the cool of the evening, walked beside us. 'Maxwellton braes are bonny,' sang the curate, 'Where early falls the dew,' and the other voices took it up, the deep voices of the few fathers who were there on leave. The Sheikh's Tomb, among palm trees, was newly whitewashed, gleaming against the dark green of the pomegranate bushes. My donkey had a carpet-covered saddle, a shiny leather pommel. Our shadows stretched out blue before us, bluer than the sea, hyacinthine; the ears of the donkey shadows shook, their patient feet dug on. Dusk came with a softness and a kindness over the salty harshness of the country, over the brilliance of the day. Evening fell in a cataclysm of splendour.

In July came a night of magic and no Joneses. Roused at ten o'clock at night, we were taken down to the shore to see the phosphorescent lights. They had been described to us, but I had been unable to imagine them beforehand. Light sprang out of the dark wet sand as we walked on it; we trod as saints tread, rayed in light. We rushed into the sea and a trail of brightness followed us; the water broke in light before us. We could not believe it; we could not have enough of it. Small waves broke gleaming, rolled in in darkness outlined in a lace of light. We leapt in and out, scattering the darkness, spreading the light like creators, like makers of the world. I wandered away from Judy and from Alethea, in an ecstasy of fantasy. I was Lucifer, the light-bringer. I was God making the world. 'Let there be light! Let there be light! Let there be light!' I shouted, dancing on the wet sand to make it so. 'Let there be light, light, light!' Curves, arcs, sweeps of light, coming and going so often as I willed it, trod it, danced it, stamped it. My mother's voice came faintly down the shore in the mild darkness, but it seemed to have nothing to do with me. 'Darling, where are you? Priscilla!' I was alone in primal chaos, in a darkness which I alone could make ordered and light. The waves, milder than the mild air of night, rolled in from the shallow sea. The smell of mussels came faintly from a stranded sandbank, the salty water lingered on my legs. 'Let there be light, light, light!' A part of me is there still, dancing in solitary luxury a great pattern of light across the darkness of the flat wet sand.

In France the armies were locked in the terrible motionless struggle that was to decide all our fates, and the dreadful death rolls mounted. An entire generation of young men was dying, spilled out like water in the appalling Stygian abyss of those unspeakable trenches. On this halcyon coast it all seemed very far away. The summer which in Europe must have seemed so endless passed all too quickly here. Autumn and the September winds set in. The sea crept perceptibly higher, one morning it went right round behind the huts, very nearly reached the canal and isolated us. Feluccas came from further along the coast to ship the great piles of water-melons brought from inland in camel loads and pyramided on the shore;

bateek, green-skinned, with bright pink flesh and black dia-
mond-shaped seeds, all water and sickliness, I hated their
taste, and chemaum, the yellow-skinned ones with white flesh
that were not much better. The mangoes ripened, we ate them
in bathing dresses before entering the sea, the best way to eat
a ripe mango. The autumn gales made whirlpools in the
sands, I had been in a small one myself, until my father pulled
me out, one went round and round and there seemed to be no
exit; it had been an unpleasant experience. We were warned to
look out for them, to bathe in the well-known pools until the
sea went down and was calm again.

On a morning like other mornings except that it was
windier, a terrible alarm went round the camp. Mrs Blunt and
Mr Sharman, bathing late and near the canal mouth, where
their huts were situated, had failed to return. Everybody had
of course been sitting not far off, but had failed to look up.
Mrs Sharman was unwell, she had not bathed with them.
Colonel Blunt had been playing golf. A non-swimmer, he
strode powerless through the shallows; his face, always red,
was crimson with desperation, his blue eyes protruded in
anguish, he made suggestions and contradicted them. 'He's
beside himself,' Mary West said, 'poor gentleman; and it's not
to be wondered at.' My father had gone with the others in the
search.

All seemed ragged and on edge. Hugh Blunt never came to
the children's lunch, which was late and badly cooked, the
younger waiters were helping in the search. Rest seemed very
long, there was no story reading, and nobody bathed before

tea. Nobody seemed able to do anything but wait about, talking in uneasy groups. I wandered down to the sea's edge with Judy and we added a desultory moat to an old castle. It was over Alethea that the lightning of this strange storm first broke. Her dolls were sitting in an orderly row along the rug-covered lid of the trunk where the linen was kept, when they were suddenly brushed aside by my mother flinging it open in a desperate quest for blankets. What could have happened to make her do such a thing? She was always a respecter of the property of others, an understander that the dolls were real people not thus cavalierly to be treated. It was as if the earth had very slightly quaked.

Late in the afternoon my father came home, after swimming and searching for hours along the coast. The two drowned bodies had at length been found. They must, I knew, be buried before nightfall tomorrow. But where, in all that lonely coast, the grown-ups asked, was holy ground to be found? Perhaps Mr Armstrong would bless a bit under the palm-trees. It was peaceful enough there, lonely and beautiful and remote. Mary West shook her head. 'They'll have to take them to Cairo or Alexandria,' she opined. 'There's Damietta,' one of the nannies said, 'perhaps there . . .'

My father sat in a deck-chair under the awning of our hut, unmoving and spent, his towel dressing-gown wrapped around him. My mother had gone to get him a hot drink and some food. His face was drawn with sadness and exhaustion; his eyes, fixed upon nothing visible, had never looked so blue. Somewhere, I knew, even outside books, lived the kind of child who at this point would have fauntleroyed up to him and cheered him with their loving words and fearless childish grace. I was none such. I took one look at that blue abstracted gaze and opted out of adult grief and pain. I collected some boon companions about me and we went stravaguing off west into the sunset. Death had uttered his ugly irrevocable sentence full in our faces, and there seemed to be no ladder up to a jewelled city of welcome, only a friend's kind mother lying in a rush-matting hut with a sheet over her and her gentle and unjudging eyes fast shut. I hastened to put the greatest possible distance between myself and this. Seven miles away upon Cape Burullos the lighthouse was a black pencil against the blaze of the west. Land-crabs rose up out of the sand and scuttled into the sea before us, their periscope eyes peering watchfully from the shallows. Pale pink mussel shells, delicate and transparent, scrunched below our horny feet. We went west and further west into a brilliant world of light and colour, collecting cowries, scallops, cockle shells, painted tops, and those small purple shells that the Phoenicians used so long ago to dye their festal robes.

XVI

To be ten years old, and in double figures, was stupendous, a landmark, almost a coming of age. The autumn of 1918 was also, although this seemed less momentous, crowned by the Armistice, declared on November 11th between Germany and the Allied Powers. Cairo reacted splendidly to this event. There were fireworks, peace processions, thanksgiving services, and jamborees of every kind. There was a Charlie Chaplin film in the open air, the first cinema I had ever seen, and so unspeakably and gloriously funny that Alethea and I repeatedly fell off our chairs, and our father and mother were not in much better case. The Greeks and the Italians, neither of whom had played a conspicuously glorious part in the struggle, held rival victory processions of great splendour through the streets of Cairo which unluckily encountered each other and refused to give way, and there was considerable bloodshed and many casualties, none of which happily proved fatal. King Fuad gave a banquet at the Abdin Palace at which there were pink sugar aeroplanes all down the middle of the table. The students at Al Azhar demonstrated, some against the British Army's continued presence and others for the hell of it, and several of them stabbed each other in the mêlée. The guns boomed out in salutes and the sirens roared in triumph, and a number of small shops were looted while no one was looking. Finally there was an immense blow-out at the Sporting Club in Gezira to which all British subjects were bidden.

It was to be on December 17th, thus economically combining itself with Christmas without arousing religious passions, and was called Celebration Day. We anticipated it for weeks and it did not disappoint. There were presents for all the children, distributed by Father Christmas out of a sack which was constantly and visibly replenished by Mr Boland. The Cypriot and Maltese children, rather more fly than their fellow Britons from Britain, lined themselves up several times over in the queue for presents and got away with it, as no one was able to identify them. This was felt to be unfair by recognisable characters like Alethea and myself, and the two celluloid dolls that came our way were received with a certain reserve, although, christened Joyce and Andrew, they subsequently became valued members of the community. I had a conversation with General Allenby about the surprising lilies like white daffodils that grew out of the sand at Brulos. Allenby was large anyway and seemed larger just then, fresh from his spectacular triumph in the plain of Esdraelon, a mighty man of valour. He had a clipped moustache and a square conventional soldierly handsomeness, penetrated by an interested and enjoying look. His mind, Lawrence wrote, was like the prow of the *Mauretania*: there was so much weight behind it that it did not need to be sharp like a razor. The last thing he was likely to have done was to stand around making jokes about fishing while Damascus burned, in order to discredit the Arabs, as he is shown doing in the *Lawrence of Arabia* film. In actual fact he arrived at Damascus some hours after the fire, made by the retreating German engineers burning their supply dumps, was out. Hot-tempered, yes, malicious, no. It was impossible not to like and admire him, so burly, interested, and kind; but the conversation became, on my side, increasingly abstracted as I could see out of the tail of my eye that the Cypriot children were eating all the macaroons. Sated with strong food, I was afterwards introduced by my father to Slatin Pasha, newly back from Vienna, a small, bird-faced, droop-eyed Austrian who had been one of General Gordon's provincial governors, and had been captured by the Mahdi after Gordon's death at Khartoum. Enslaved and held captive by the Khalifa for twelve years, used as a running syce, and under constant threat of death, he had embraced Islam at the point of the sword, an action generally considered to be not quite cricket. (But for those of us who are not saints it is one thing to be martyred before an eager crowd of several thousand people assembled for the purpose, a dozen of whom are certain to be taking notes and writing to the Pope, and quite another to be rubbed out by an arbitrary chieftain in an obscure part of Africa, with no one present except a few Sudanese indifferently scratching their backsides.) And here he was, a cheerful small bird of a man, back in the bosom of the Church of Rome, and cosily eating chocolate eclairs with a teaspoon, a monument to human indestructibility. Soon the fireworks shrieked upwards, fell in a golden fusillade of light; victory seemed a beautiful thing and I hoped it would go on for ever. The palm trees above the swings, illuminated in a wild glow, were larger than life. It was late before we were in bed, stupefied by jellies, ice-cream, orangeade, fireworks, meringues, and the cessation of hostilities. Everything whirled round in my head, and for once even the majestic cadences of the Authorized Version failed to lull and soothe. Too much food raged furiously together in my stomach and my head was full of Catherine wheels. 'Cheer up,' my father said, summoned to my bedside, to hear my dying words (which came out disappointingly as 'Ow! Gosh! Ow!') 'it's a poor heart that never over-eats itself. And after all,' he added, 'it's a famous victory.'

This winter, encouraged by a book with stirring illustrations called *Erling the Bold,* we and the Westropp children decided to become Norse gods. There was keen competition for the only sympathetic character in the hierarchy, Baldur the Beautiful, who in an Ibsenish manner gets killed right at the outset. The twins were Odin and Thor, deities who seem to lack individuality, but who must at one time have had some kind of drive, in order to get Wednesday and Thursday called after them. Alethea was Freya, who at least had Friday to her credit, and I was a sinister deity called Loki who incessantly put spokes into the wheels of everyone else and never even achieved a weekday. Valhalla soon palled, and we became Ancient Britons. This excellent game has only one snag; it is quite impossible to play it when actually in Britain, owing to the exigencies of the climate. Here it could be played on the roof of our house, which was large, flat, situated on various levels, and surrounded by a parapet, and also by the thick branches of the eucalyptus trees, which, planted at about the time of my birth, were now a hundred feet high. The grown-ups had, we knew, a strange fad against nakedness, but surely no one could mind it on a roof? To be an Ancient Briton it is essential to be stark and to be painted bright blue. The Britons must have had rather larger paint brushes than we had; it took a full morning to get into battle array. All too soon the cobalt and ultramarine in our paint-boxes would run out, and the younger ones – oh, the shame of it, with the Germans so lately our enemies – had to put up with Prussian blue, mutter they never so loudly. Once arrayed we held chariot battles, Caractacus *v.* Boadicea, not minding whether these two monarchs did or did not actually coincide in epoch or meet in battle. The youngest Westropp, who was called Toony, had a spirited rendering of one of Boadicea's daughters, with flashing teeth and a flashing sword and Prussian blue running wildly down her midriff. But Mohammed, acting for the first time in recorded history as an enemy, put a stop to this game, complaining to my mother that it was sacrilegious, and disturbing to the morale of the policeman outside the Russells' house, and altogether involved the household of my father in a serious loss of face.

Mary West left, not very deeply lamented, promoted into a full-scale Nanny to a baby called Lewis Dawnay, for whom she began instantly to crochet a nightdress case with entwined initials, L.D., on it. She was succeeded by Annie MacNichol, who came from a poor home on the outskirts of Edinburgh, where she had learned more goodness than I would ever know. She had great red rough hands, which, as I frequently told her, were like newly cooked lobsters. I stuck my elbows into them when I knelt to say my prayers at night. She was a Presbyterian, and may have thought that kneeling was idolatry; nothing came back at me from her warm face surrounded by fuzzy hair but a look of sympathetic worship, of understanding love. If the heaven that lies about us in our infancy is its non-lasting ability to love the unlovable, affectionate three-year-old arms embracing the scraggy dew-lapped necks of the indifferent old, warm kisses showered upon soured repulsive faces, there is also something heaven-sent in the power of children to discern and celebrate goodness and warmth of heart wherever it truly exists. Not yet have they begun to resent goodness for its power to show up what is less good in themselves, nor learned to despise it for its unsuccess. The reign of Annie MacNichol came in like an age of gold. Nursery life ran smooth for a while; I even found myself cleaning my teeth without having to be told.

Everything, now that it was practically peace, seemed freer and less urgent, and as we walked in the fields in the brightness of the winter afternoons, people still looked up from their work to bless us as we passed. But in fact the strains and grievances that the war had brought were not yet redressed, and politically all was going far from well. The British Protectorate over Egypt, never intended as a permanent arrangement, had been proclaimed as an emergency measure at the outbreak of war. Now Roushdy Pasha, the wise and liberal Egyptian Prime Minister, proposed that he and Adly Pasha, then Minister of Foreign Education, should go to London to lay before the British Government proposals for the future government of Egypt. Wingate warmly supported this request, but the British Government turned it down. It was too busy. This was perhaps where the long and sad divorce began.

The British Government had reason on its side, and lacked only understanding. It was better, logically, to dispose of the urgent problems of a devastated Europe, and to postpone the question of the future government of Egypt until a more convenient time. 'But', my father wrote, 'logical considerations have very little weight when a whole nation feels itself insulted and humiliated.' It was a great loss of face for Roushdy Pasha, especially as other delegations from neighbouring countries were welcomed in London. 'They will receive an Archbishop and six grocers from Cyprus,' the cry of Cairo went up, 'but they won't receive Egyptian Ministers.' It was the opportunity for which the extremists had been waiting. Saad Zaghloul Pasha came forward with his war-cry of '*Istiklal el tam!*' A number of delighted adherents echoed this call for complete independence. By the time the British Government got around to receiving Roushdy Pasha he was obliged to ask that they should also receive Saad. This was refused. Roushdy, who had level-headedly steered the Egyptian government through its wartime difficulties, was forced to resign. Mohammed Said, his successor, resigned as a protest against the coming of the Milner Commission, and the charming and popular

Youssef Wahba, who might have been the necessary reconciler, was shortly driven out of office by ill-health, to the regret of all. As so often happens when one bad mistake has been made, a chain of untoward events followed on it, almost as if the Devil, having cleverly made his opening, were allowed a free run, so that it must end in the bitterness of bloodshed, and of an estrangement and a hatred that need never have been.

It was March, a hot breathless pre-hamseen morning. While our parents strove, through the heat of spring, with wisdom, patience, and calm, to bring about an understanding, something of the tension in the air twanged also in our responsive heart strings. The Nile was very low, as it is in spring, unlike any other river in the world; a circumstance which caused such a headache to Herodotus, who hit upon the right explanation but was quite unable to believe himself. It was a day for wickedness. Alethea, somehow guessing this, had sensibly retired to the roof and was writing a play about Omar Khayyam. An ideal companion in every game of the imagination, she sometimes baulked at action, and tended to withdraw during my bouts of aggression, to play dolls' picnics with the gentle and diffident Camilla Russell, or make mud pies with Margaret Amos. I was not above dolls' picnics myself, in softer moods, with miniature oranges on nasturtium leaf plates, nor yet mud pies, made ready for baking out of the silk-soft black Egyptian earth, but there were mornings when my soul cried out for stronger meat, and this was one. I wanted a non-family morning of intense action.

There was a restlessness about this hot Saturday forenoon.

I transplanted a couple of verbenas into a different part of my garden, watering them carefully in, but even the feel of the fine friable earth between my fingers had lost its savour. In their hutch in one of the open arches of the potting shed where the rabbits lived out their lettuce lives, Farouk, an Angora, was listlessly munching. Born on the same day as that hapless monarch, the Angora had been named after him. Farouk himself, still cotbound in the Ismailia Palace, had been pronounced on the nanny-circuit, and even by my mother, to be a perfectly lovely baby. Which, as the nannies all subsequently said, about thirty years later, all goes to show. Although not all lovely babies lose their fathers when they are sixteen and are handed absolute financial power over many millions.

Hugh Blunt, possessed by the same heat-driven restlessness, chose this moment to appear. He urged me to come down and look for shells on the bare river banks. This was forbidden ground. We were not, and this was an absolute rule, allowed outside the gates alone; nor did we much want to go. Taken often to Cairo, round the Muskey, the Citadel, and the mosques, sailing down-river past Em-baba to buy earthenware pots near the Barrage, we had met sufficiently frightening sights. We did not want to encounter alone the moaning blind men, the drug-driven, the dreadfully deformed bodies dragging themselves about for alms, the whole seething scarifying world of an eastern city. Once at Port Said we had been witnesses of mob violence, than which there is scarcely a more horrifying sight. Waiting in the hotel for a ship delayed in the Red Sea, we had seen a young man fleeing for his life along the waterfront, pursued by a shouting mob. He had climbed frantically up a lamp post, had been dragged down, had disappeared from view, was glimpsed again, limp and powerless, his legs and arms trussed up by the crowd who were about to throw him into the deep water of the harbour to drown helplessly. Tarbooshed policemen with truncheons had appeared to save him in the nick of time, and the Port Said crowd, bored by the rule of law, had very nearly thrown them in too. Then there was the booby man, a pitch black Nubian who wandered round Gezira playing boob-boob-boob on a strange string harp, probably perfectly harmlessly; but his coal-blackness and his wild eyes filled us with terror because they were so outlandish and excessive. So that, one way and another, we had not the appetite to wander off on our own. Just across the road and down the river bank in full sight of the house in the company of Hugh could be construed as being different. Had not my mother urged me to be kind to Hugh in view of his loss?

The Nile was now, comparatively, a trickle. Layer on layer, the black-grey earth of its banks spread down many feet to what was now, in this branch of its course, a moderate English-sized river. There seemed to be no shells, or no interesting ones, just the usual big blue slatey ones, rather like horse mussels. We wandered desultorily along the flotsam bank. The morning heat thickened. Hugh's hair which was his bane, very fair and curly, was dampened into tight dark coils. Feluccas, waiting for the noon opening of the bridge, gathered alongside one another. The voices of the felucca men, jockeying for position, floated back up to the river to us.

'I dare you', Hugh suddenly said, 'to drink some water from the Nile.'

'Don't be a silly ass. We'd die of poison.'

'Go on. I dare you.'

'Of course I won't. It's filthy dirty stinking stuff.'

'Go on. Can't you take a dare?'

So easy to refuse it. One had only to utter the magic formula, 'Feigns the dare'. Honour would thus be satisfied, prestige maintained.

'I would have thought', Hugh said, 'that you could take a dare now you were ten.'

The hot wind blew faintly off the desert, prelude of worse and hotter. More feluccas had arrived at the bridge. The felucca men were shouting at each other as they lowered their huge sails.

'Girls', Hugh said, 'are a feeble lot.'

The black rich mud was powder underfoot. I dug it with the sharp edge of my sandal. Some of the sand went in. I hopped about on one leg, shaking it out. If the Egyptians could drink the Nile, unfiltered, out of their hands, why could not I? I moved several yards upstream, away from this thought.

'Go on then. I dare you. No one is looking. No one will know. I dare you to drink it.'

I gave up trying to get the sand out of my sandals and scuffed a whole lot more in. The sun shone down in force and some flies had found us out and pursued us.

'Nanny's darling,' Hugh said.

I had a sudden picture of all that carefully filtered water, all those saucepans of laboriously scalded milk, all those permanganated lettuce leaves and fruit, all that ceaseless babyish Nanny vigilance. I dismissed from my mind the recollection that English children in Egypt did quite often die of savage diseases, that a family who were well-known to us had recently gone to the wrong hotel in Port Said because the right one was full and that their youngest little girl had there contracted bubonic plague and died within hours. Away with all this tedious fuss, fuss, fuss. I bent down and scooped up a double handful of the Nile, Hugh doing likewise (for the darer has always to accept the dare himself), and drank it to the dregs. To swallow it took all the obstinacy I had. It was nearly opaque, tasted indescribable, had drained, since its source, several thousand villages, and was probably full of bilharzia flukes. We drank because it was the most forbidden thing we could think of to do. It did neither of us any harm whatever.

This unforgivable action, probably more interesting to Freud than to anyone else, effected a kind of release. We ran along the river banks past the feluccas and hid below the Zamalek bridge. The noise of the rattling carts and the shouts of donkey boys crossing the bridge came hollowly down to us. Here I had a very definite sense of being dangerously out of bounds. Hiding palls after about two minutes, when no one is looking for you. Under the bridge it was dark and riverish, and smelt of chewed sugar cane and donkey piss.

Somewhere about now Mervyn Molesworth joined the

party, and somewhere about now the Devil entered in. Mervyn perhaps arrived slightly first, but the Devil may have slipped in with the Nile water. Mervyn was carrying a pistol. He had a dark round head, dark round eyes, bright red cheeks, and a liberal portion of original sin. He was good company, a handy mender of bicycle punctures, and without malice. Our delinquency somehow multiplied itself together, we egged each other on, delightedly showing off to each other. Hugh had the excuse of his drowned mother; we had not even that. Our mothers were present and available; constant, loving, and kind; but just at that moment superintending the making of fig jam and supposing us to be happily playing in the garden. We cast about gleefully for some harm to inflict.

Beyond the Zamalek bridge there were some feluccas unloading. Women with baskets upon their heads were transporting earthenware pots from the river bank to carts which waited on the road. Other women carried also, on their heads, sacks of earth. In general I liked the Egyptians; laughed with their laughter, and sympathized with the recurrent disasters which so often seemed to accompany the simplest operations of their lives, but this morning the entire human race felt like so much cannon-fodder. As they worked, the women sang their habitual monotonous chant. It sounded like Ha-Ya, Ha-Ya, Dinny Ah Ma. A wave of furious derision swept over us. Unexpectedly, without warning, we hated their foreignness, their patience, the futile docility of their lives, their uncomplaining beast-of-burden-ness, their inability, in six thousand years, to think up more than one line, sung on more than

three notes. Seizing up imaginary baskets, we aped their graceful swaying walk up the river bank, the dignified movement
with which they swung their heavy baskets down from off
their heads. Ha-Ya, Ha-Ya, Dinny Ah Ma, we shouted and
yelled, over and over again. Ha-Ya, Ha-Ya, Dinny Ah Ma.
Our voices took on without difficulty the nasal hopeless tone.
We capered and leapt in the soft black sand in an ecstasy of
derision. Our mocking voices rang out; we strove to out-shout
each other, intoxicated by the heat and the stenchy Nile water
and the obvious effect we were making. A line of poetry
cropped up at the back of my mind, but I told it to shut up
and it obeyed. 'Oxus forgetting the bright speed he knew.'
What had that to do with me? Ha-Ya, Ha-Ya, Dinny Ah Ma,
we echoed. 'Sing,' Hugh shouted, inspired by living in prox-
imity to the C. in C.'s camp, 'sing something bloody else!'

Anger was building up amongst the felucca crews; having
successfully got our rise we moved hastily away across the
fields to seek fresh damage to inflict. As it was by now very
very hot, we naturally hit upon the idea of making a fire. This
we did, of bamboo sticks, in the potting shed, which although
a very large open room, was *under* our house, the idea being
to reproduce, as far as is possible without an actual victim, a
cannibal feast. The notion of employing one of my dolls, or
one of Alethea's, for this purpose, had been mooted; but I was
too good a mother, and too good an aunt. We burned instead
a sack of dry berseem. It looked satisfactorily alive as it curled
up in the heat. Shortly before the house could actually catch
fire, Mohammed smelt the burning smell, and appeared.

Calling upon the compassion and the faithfulness of God, he doused the fire, and urged us in round terms never to be so daft again. It was the first time in the ten years we had spent under the same roof that I had ever seen Mohammed really angry with me. The little pox-mark holes all over his face that generally gave him a freckled friendly look seemed to deepen and grow painful with his rage; I might, but for the presence of the others, have cried. 'No more, Lady,' he concluded, switching dramatically into English at the close of his peroration. We had the sense to drift away, under the eucalyptuses, past the borders and the summerhouse, through the rose garden and out into the government garden and the renewed temptations of the Boulac Road.

The government garden's head gardener, Hassan, was a friend of mine, and if he had been there we might have calmed down. He was cheerful, thick-lipped, and immensely strong; to see him dig a trench or cut down a tree was like seeing a bulldozer in action. He was, besides, a conversationalist, and interested in trees. In the quiet of noon I used to sit cross-legged under a shady tree with him and his colleagues, eating enormous bites of the delicious flat unleavened bread which he brought with him wrapped in a red cotton handkerchief, dismissing the thought of what Nanny's reaction to this germ-rife snack would have been. In return I brought him Turkish cigarettes filched out of the silver box in the drawing-room. I could understand only about a quarter of the talk, which was perhaps as well; what came through seemed very jolly. He was a superb gardener, and a friendly and firm character, but alas, on this hot morning he was absent.

We repaired to a separate and unfrequented part of the garden which was used for growing young trees, and which had
just been watered. It was surrounded by formidable spike-
topped iron railings and ran along the Boulac Road. Along
this moved the usual flow of flat carts on their way to Cairo,
covered with cross-legged black-veiled women, incessantly
chatting, like a load of starlings. There was generally a man
leading or driving the mule or the tiny donkey that strained
along pulling the load. This common sight aroused in us on
this ill-starred morning a strong desire to bully, a kind of
fiendish exultation of scorn and enmity. We collected large
piles of well-compacted mud balls, which we launched, from
behind the perfect safety of the iron railings, into the chattering parties as they rode by. The effect was gratifyingly great.
The noise increased a hundredfold and the women rose to
their feet and wrung their hands and called down curses and
dropped their baskets off the carts and screamed. The men
shouted and fumed, and cursed at us in a furious torrent of
outraged Arabic. Our spirits mounted with their rage. The
pace of action quickened, there was hardly time to keep up the
supply of mud balls. Alethea had been reft away from Omar
Khayyam and was throwing mud balls with the best. One of
the drivers left his cart and went round to the nearest house
and complained to the suffragi there, Yusef, a lazy individual
with a sallow face who replied that it was nothing to do with
him and that in any case it was his morning for polishing the
silver. 'Don't hit the trams,' Mervyn said, 'only the trailers.

The trams might have English soldiers in them.' We were impressed by this responsible command. More and more carts kept pouring along; it was ludicrous and delightful to see what consternation each assault caused.

A tall angry driver with a deeply pock-marked face tied up his ass to a tree and crossed the road to see if he could get at us. He came close to the railings and leant through suddenly to grab our legs. His eyes, perhaps hashish-filled, rolled with passion; it was clear from his expression that if he could have laid hands on us he would have killed us. It was also perfectly clear that he could not. The sensation was infinitely enjoyable. The women on the cart shrieked imprecations; the donkey joined in by braying deafeningly at a passing friend. A kind of furious darkness gathered in the man's face. We faced each other through the railings, the pith and bitterness of racial chance summed up in us; sturdy fair-skinned ten-year-olds, with a thousand years of wind and rain and good food behind us, and a thin, white-robed, dark-skinned man with six thousand years of hot sun and short commons behind him, and the iron Lancashire-made railings in between. He gave us a last look, spat through what seemed to be tightly clenched teeth, and went his way.

This game, which had not even begun to pall, was abruptly and dramatically brought to a stop. With a mud ball poised in my hand, ready to let fly, I became aware of a dark-blue-suited long-legged figure advancing down the Boulac Road from Cairo with a familiar stride. I recognized with horror that it was my father. What could have brought him? He often walked back across the river from the Ministry in Cairo, having an Englishman's passion for stretching his legs, but never before half-past one or two o'clock; lunch was always late for him. And today the noon gun at the Citadel had barely gone! I perceived at once that here was the hand of God, so often canvassed by the grown-ups yet so rarely visible in real life. I dropped my mud ball like a hot coal, and called the attention of Hugh and Mervyn and Alethea. We faded instantly into the landscape. There was just a chance that my father had been too far away to see what we were about. I knew very well what his reaction would be, and I feared him very much, as well as loving him. His anger could be terrible, a level flail of words. I had felt the sting of his tongue once or twice, and never forgotten. When I was seven he had come upon me imitating Ismaïn and Mahmoud at their noonday devotions. A Moslem at prayer, with the accompanying gymnastics, is an object of irresistible comedy to a mocking child brought up in a different religious tradition. Up and down, and back on the heels, and forward again with the forehead pressed on the ground. Don't, Alethea had said, knowing instinctively better, but I had pressed on, intoxicated with the wittiness of my performance. My father had appeared with long strides across the lawn, and what had to be said on the subject of respect for the religious observances of others was said swiftly, fiercely, and for ever; my innocence of offence was taken as no excuse. I was now deeply apprehensive. I went back with Mervyn to his house, and here, not being old enough for a quick drink, we stiffened our morale with enormous slices of bread and butter thickly covered with brown sugar. This effectively spoiled our lunches, and brought an uncomprehending reproach to the kind face of Annie MacNichol.

No retribution fell upon us, as I had made certain that it would. We had simply not been seen, and Yusef was too idle to tell the tale. Nor were we aware of having probably undone, in one morning's work, the goodwill built up slowly and patiently by our dedicated parents over many years. All that I knew was that the eye of God, trusty weapon of the grown-ups, did indeed see everywhere. It had seen us tormenting the Egyptians and its inflexible beam had directed my father to leave the Ministry an hour and a half ahead of schedule and prevent us. Not again did I utter so much as a harsh word to an Egyptian. God saw everywhere, my father was his instrument, and life was altogether more formidable a business than I had previously thought.

XVII

'After Kantara', I wrote to my father from Port Said, 'there were hundreds and hundreds of men working on the line,' thus supplying him, for the first and last time, with a piece of useful information. As soon as our train had passed, the men pulled up the rails. The 1919 rising had begun, and this was part of a plan concerted in the war in the event of a Turkish invasion from the Sinai Peninsula. Its only result in the present situation was to bring the poorer people of Cairo who bought their food in small amounts at a time, within measurable distance of starvation, but it must have been satisfying to the men who did it. '*Istiklal el tam!*' There is nothing like pulling up a railway line to make one feel one is really going places.

The rising was directed against the Army of Occupation and not against the government, and had never any chance of success but might well have involved terrible bloodshed. The British army had not yet settled into its role of always being shot at and never shooting back. Exhausted by four years of bloody war, bored by delayed demobilisation, fearful over the prospect of finding jobs in civilian life, longing for home, it had now to sit tight and accept the isolated murders of its members. Sixteen were caught unarmed and chopped up at the outset, and sporadic shootings continued. The foreign

271

community marvelled. 'For half of this, for one quarter of this,' Charles de Rocca Serra, a French colleague of my father's at the Ministry, told him, 'for a fragment of such treatment a French army would have laid all Cairo in ashes.' The situation was saved by the sanity, nerve, and clemency of Allenby. 'Only for him telling us,' the corporal in charge of the picket on Zamalek bridge told my father, 'only for him and we'd have . . . the . . . s good and proper. He takes his risks, see, same as the rest of us, up in Palestine, always did. He said it wouldn't do no good to kill a lot of them. Said they'd got their grievances and that. He come round all the barracks and told us so himself. But only for him, see, only for him.'

British officials, although not threatened, were urged to carry revolvers.

'Do, now, Will,' my mother urged him. But he saw no point. He was not, he pointed out, going to shoot any Egyptians anyway, and if they shot him it would be sure to be from behind, and all that would mean would be their helping themselves to another revolver off his body. 'But Will, if it's *known* that you all carry one that would at least discourage them from shooting?' The ones that shoot, he maintained, were not open to reason. He laughed, and my mother shook her head at him as we got into the train.

Once more the P. & O. liner swung out of the Suez canal, past the statue of Ferdinand de Lesseps, into the roads of Port Said, whither the lighter bore us to embark; S.S. *Kaiser-i-Hind,* untouched by the hand of time, wearing the half diamond flag; de-camouflaged, painted black as to funnels and hull, buff as to superstructure. All, after two and a half years, was the same; wiry lascars and a stout chief steward, the pattern on the red carpet stools in the first-class cabins, and the taste of the fluffy apples that came with the early morning tea. Like Egypt, the *Kaiser-i Hind* was full of soldiers, but unlike Egypt it was scrubbed and austere, and subject to wartime regulations. Lunch was in two sittings, and there was margarine for tea instead of butter. The soldiers boxed on the boat deck and the sea was very rough. There was a day's peace between the yellow bastions of Malta, and then on to Gibraltar and the Atlantic. The passengers could almost be felt to be bracing themselves for England, for the chill of the blackthorn winter, for the rations, the bereaved faces, for the whipping winds of spring. The sea was free of German submarines, but not yet clear of mines. Entering the Bay of Biscay the ship hove to, in order to put on what I think was called a paravane, a kind of cow-catcher for drifting mines. As I lay in my bunk there was another of those sickening shattering crashes that send the heart of the ignorant and nervous voyager racing up into his throat. My heart stayed there, banging like a hammer, for what felt like five minutes, before returning with choking deliberation to its usual position. I made myself a promise that if ever we reached harbour I would never again venture on the sea. Slowly we turned on to our course. The seas smacked along the side of the ship with a kind of purposeful malevolence, grey monsters swinging tirelessly at us. I felt a renewed reverence for Erling the Bold, Christopher Columbus, Drake, etc.

The haven, when reached, was disappointing and chilly, customs sheds at Southampton with the remains of snow on their roofs. I had never seen snow close to before; it was stuff only known on Christmas cards, or covering high mountains seen distantly from out at sea. Quarantine held us on board for a further forty-eight hours; the passengers, deck-bound, could be heard excitedly sentimentalising the scene. 'Look, a good old English policeman! Isn't that jolly? Look, a good old English loafer!' Their comments seemed quite daft and their noses had gone red; I drew away from them and regarded my native land with disfavour. Some strange customs regulation forbade the taking of sugar from Egypt which had a huge sur-plus, to England, which had been rationed for years and had practically none. My mother took no notice of this official dottiness and smuggled in a large quantity in a tin travelling bath, sweeping through the customs house, where at last she could commune with officials in her native tongue, with the greatest confidence and aplomb. For the first time for four years her son and her nephews and nieces and all dependents had as much toffee as they could eat, and her sisters delight-edly made green gooseberry jam.

England, after so long, was a stranger country, and William, met at Waterloo, was a stranger boy. Fed lavishly on un-rationed food in Egypt, I had grown as tall as him; we both found this disconcerting. We stood apart, wanting, but not quite liking, to have a good stare. He was silent and aloof and seemed more like someone else's brother. We, I expect, seemed like someone else's sisters, brown and self-confident and colonial and probably very peculiarly dressed. Necessarily, he had grown a kind of self-containment. His brain, however, was not of a calibre to be affected by adversity, and when the time came he got his Winchester scholarship without any apparent effort, coming out always half an hour before the end of the allotted time.

I had still a faint hope that our cousins would all miraculously have stayed still and allowed me to catch up. But it was only William's stature that had done this. They seemed to have got even further ahead, were full of Zeppelin stories and unimpressed with any faint saga I could produce about submarines. 'You never actually saw one, did you?' they said, and I was obliged to admit that I never actually had. All were taller, or solider, or differently dressed. Jack, it was even rumoured, was going to be married. Rodney had picked up a strange germ from an Indian in a field hospital and was never to be permanently well again; the remote world of intermittent ill-health now held him. Phyllis no longer had a father, her hair was sometimes up, and attack had become her best defence. Betty qualified as what was now known as a flapper, her hair tied back behind her ears in a wide black flapping bow. Tony, having broken nearly all his bones in a bicycle accident just before the naval entrance examination, had failed to get into Dartmouth, was going to Sandhurst. Tall, very silent, and deft, he remained mysteriously engaging, with a deep voice and a full programme of sporting activities in which he occasionally permitted one to take a minor part. Peggy Barnard, sent away to a convent boarding school and arriving late for chapel one morning, had locked the Mother Superior, the nuns, and all the other children into the chapel, thrown the key into the rain-water barrel and spent a happy morning in bed with a bag of bulls-eyes and a good book. She was consequently back at home again with a considerable increase of panache. Harry, still under the reproach of being delicate, continued to take no notice, tirelessly climbing trees and rocks and emerging from icy seas in which he had stayed longer than anyone else, blue all over and resolutely refusing to get the chills, bronchitis, and pneumonia which were confidently predicted for him.

Most changed of all was Hamer. Bereft of his excellent tiger-hunting father and landed instead with a seraphic baby brother who seemed to absorb all the attention, he had fallen victim to a bloody-mindedness which I was too soon to know myself. His brother's new Nanny had been with Will and Michael Goodenough, and belaboured his ears with tales of their outstanding intelligence and unfailing charm, arousing in him a grim determination to conceal as well as he could his considerable natural endowment of both these two qualities, to be as stupid and un-charming as possible. He fought everyone; and the larger they were the better. He tyrannized over everyone else, and to answer back was simply to ask for more. At Sidmouth he would dive off the high breakwater into raging rough seas from which he was hauled by kindly and officious passers-by, to whom he protested furiously that it was practically a flat calm. 'The tide was coming in anyway, and there are no currents here, and I was simply swimming around,' he complained, dripping and defiant, to his rescuers. He had a way of reciting 'The Assyrian came down like a wolf on the fold', in a fiery and sinister manner that sent shivers down the spine and would probably have delighted Lord Byron. 'Now I'll show you how girls recite,' and he would go on to repeat the poem in a lisping falsetto that I found infinitely galling. 'No !' I would cry, rising like a fish, 'No! That's not how girls recite, that's not! Listen!' But he wouldn't listen. He would slope off to go fishing in the Test (for this was at Winchester), or to quarrel with William over their railway systems or butterfly collections. He was depressed by William's excessive intelligence, and William was depressed by his excessive fearlessness, and neither had fathers present to tell them that things iron out in time. The war, in some way or other, had affected us all. We should wear its wounds for life.

Aunt Bay was to be married again and was to return to India, this time in the role of the colonel's lady. She sang like a lark, but whether this was to do with India, or to do with Uncle Cyril, who could say? Uncle Arthur, now that the business of the Germans had been dealt with, was soon to embark upon a one-man war against the whole of the rest of the ruling body of his old college at Oxford, Christ Church, who were proposing to sell the valuable land to their immediate south for a handsome sum to a commercial developer. In this cause he endured and enjoyed some years of extreme unpopularity and very nearly got the sack from his studentship (for such is the eccentric name by which the members of the ruling body of Christ Church are known). In the end he was obliged to call in the support of all old members of the college by a letter to *The Times* containing the splendid phrase 'the lure of filthy lucre'. The reward of his victory was the opening up of the whole magnificent south aspect of Christ Church, and the making of an open War Memorial garden, for which anyone coming into Oxford from the south has cause to be grateful to him.

England, this summer, seemed to lie in a rain-washed, storm-beaten stillness, an express train shunted for the while into a disused railway siding. My father, returning for his leave, was perhaps more able to understand why nobody bothered much about Egypt. There was too much grief, loss, shock, for any immediate recovery. The food was bad and scant, and everything needed painting. There were widows everywhere, with strained pale looks, and aunts with grim lined faces who would never recover from the loss of their only sons. Dark and handsome Philip Howard, son of 'poor dear Cousin Hy', had died of wounds when the war was as good as over. All seemed on edge, rain forever fell: oh for the land-crabs and the hot afternoon winds of Brulos!

A virus infection re-converted me to England. I was taken to convalesce with an elderly spinster cousin of my mother's, who lived quite alone, in a manner then considered most eccentric, with only a daily cook, in an enchanting cottage under Vixen Tor on Dartmoor, doing oil paintings of the moor, and making delicious floury scones. In a fly from Tavistock station, drawn by a bold black horse, we lurched up the rocky valley road in the pure sweet air of a late June evening. The path up to the cottage led under a beech arch, brilliant with spring leaf. The streams fell softly below copses of stunted oak trees and scattered hazel bushes. In the valley the river Walkham roared and tumbled in clear waterfalls and deep pools between rounded moss-grown granite boulders. I drank quantities of the Walkham, it tasted very differently from the Nile. On the banks *Osmunda regalis* ferns grew, and innumerable different kinds of moss. In the mornings the cobwebs outside the cottage were all outlined in dew, the dewy grass was silk-soft underfoot. Dartmoor ponies cropped among the streams, with their foals nuzzling against them. Great rounded boulders, lichen-sprinkled, were harsh but tenable to climbing feet. Even the bracken was wonderful in its teeming greenness to eyes attuned to desert sand; even the thick mysterious mists were delightful in their strangeness, their soft clinging moisture.

Standing on a boulder in mid-stream, reciting bits out of 'The Lay of the Last Minstrel', which chimed with the falling waters, or, inexplicably, 'The Battle of the Baltic', perhaps helped to take the taste of Hamer's insults out of my mouth. I still tried, some of the time, though with waning enthusiasm, to be a boy. At other times, with no boys present to point out how soppy this was, Alethea and I contentedly became the fairies of the rowan tree.

The August holidays brought William; and Harry, whose mother was ill. Their presence involved a climbing up of the chimney of Vixen Tor to the top, and the exploration of other tors and of the sources of rivers, a return into a non-imaginary country, a boys' world of effort and endeavour. Neutral ground was arrived at in the building of a small sized Bronze Age village, out of a pile of little stones on a flat grassy space beside the stream. Covering in the course of time several square yards, it had a processional way, circular stone and moss houses, granaries, and a miniature Stonehenge in the middle. Organized by William, and called Burzel by Harry, it occupied many happy hours, prone in a Bronze Age Lilliput beside the tumbling stream.

In the autumn we were promoted into dark blue skirts and a governess, and returned to Egypt in a French liner called the *Sphinx*. It was very crowded; my mother and Alethea and I shared a cabin with Madame Groppi, wife of the famous pastry cook in Cairo. Madame Groppi, who could easily have bought up the Hayter family many times over, was excessively humble and unobtrusive, dressing in her bunk and leaving the cabin early in the morning and never returning until late at night, although pressed to do otherwise. She would not even accept the use of a hook for her dressing-gown, but kept it, neatly folded, on the end of her bunk. Fresh from Paris, she had bought quantities of delicious scent which she used in a lavish manner that my mother thought extravagant and not quite cricket. (This phrase, although I never heard it uttered, occurred frequently in books, and seemed to haunt the air of childhood.) The passage was again rough and I can never smell Lanvin's Chypre without a faint feeling of nausea. As the outline of Alexandria grew clearer in the morning haze, it was surprising to see how many smart Europeanly-dressed ladies retreated swiftly into equally smart Paris-made black veils and draperies and behind their harsh uncomfortable brass asaba.

'Why, Mother, why do they change?'

'Because they are Islamic ladies, and Egypt is Islam.'

'But if they are Islamic ladies, why do they dress like French ladies in France?'

'More comfortable,' my mother said.

'They've got bracelets on,' I said irrelevantly, 'under their silk stockings. Why do you think?'

'To keep them safe,' my mother said. 'Aren't you cold, darling, without a jersey on?' Alexandria presently claimed us, the waves of its various clamour broke over us; the Moslem ladies, subtly altered in demeanour, followed their husbands meekly ashore.

XVIII

'No creepy-crawlies in my schoolroom,' Miss G. said. She shuddered at the silkworms, who, unaware of this threat to their habitat, were busy among their mulberry leaves. She had the bright chirpy manner that presages an irritable temper, and I had the feeling already that she was going to be a mistake. She seemed to think that friendly relations could be established by always calling nightgowns nighties and referring to biscuits as bikkies. She had been with Harry and Anne Slessor, whom she adored, especially Harry; it says much for both these characters that her incessant praises of them were unable to turn us against them. They turned us against her.

'Drink up your drinkies,' she said. She wore a black velvet band round her bead, and her two front teeth were unbecomingly apart. Alethea, sweet-mannered and co-operative, and extremely good at lessons, seemed to manage to rub along with her. Alethea had a way, too, of being able to abstract herself when things became tiresome, which they not infrequently did. She was coming to have a long-necked, remote, Nefertiti cast of features; perhaps my mother had constantly visited the Cairo Museum before she was born, and I would sometimes assure her that she was really an Egyptian baby found in the bulrushes and adopted by my parents out of kindness. This never failed to produce a colossal rise. Sometimes I went too far, and Alethea had a remarkably effective line of action. 'I am going', she would say, with great finality, 'into my world.' And did. She transferred herself there without apparent difficulty and remained there, indifferent to threats or cajolements. It was a country full of interesting inhabitants and at such times I was not permitted to know what went on; though at other times I was allowed in, and even occasionally, a few tentative suggestions of mine were entertained. The only disservice she did me was to land me with a nickname. Unable as a baby to say Priscilla, she shortened it to Billa, from whence it became Bill. This seemed, at the time, rather rollicking and traditional; my father was Will, my brother was William; in a Moslem country it put one more in the movement. From adolescence onwards it became increasingly a bore.

Alethea no doubt would manage, with her on-and-off technique, to live with Miss G. But would I? In the desert beyond the fields the pyramids reassuringly stood. Comfortably the same, they bestrode the distance with their proud triangular solidity, as if human change were a thing of no moment. In the foreground the Nile incessantly wrote and unwrote little lines upon itself. Everything outside was the same. The air was warm and dry and sparkling, my hair had gone straight in it, as it always did. There were even matters of consolation within; I had gone into long stockings. It was difficult to keep the seams where they should be, but the prestige of it was great. Unluckily there were no contemporaries to whom to show them off. The dreariest thing about the presence of Miss G. was that we no longer went to school at Miss Quibell's.

After six weeks I informed my parents that the arrangement simply would not do. Unaccountably, they took no notice. Miss G. was Irish, and effectively called forth the Irish in me. One evening, doubtless not without good cause, she laid into me with a hairbrush. What makes for uncontrollable anger? The feeling perhaps, that one is threatened as a person, attacked in one's individual dignity. The hairbrush manoeuvre was not a success, and was not repeated, although the outbursts came fairly regularly. Poor Miss G. was always extremely sorry afterwards, and apologetic, which was more than I was about the events which provoked the outbursts. Tearfully she would present me with five piastres or a small brass pyramid, which was welcome but embarrassing, and left one feeling unappeased. Harry and Anne, she assured me, had loved her, but I knew myself totally unqualified for this feat. I disappeared whenever possible into the sewing-room and turned the sewing-machine handle for Annie MacNichol, who was mending the sheets, and who exuded kindness and warmth.

Miss G. was clearly here to stay, and like an oppressed minority, I resorted to guerrilla tactics. The first step was a change of identity, and here a splendid book called *The Tiger* by H. Mockler-Ferryman, came to my aid. During November 1919 I became The Tiger. All day long I lay hidden in the baking nullahs with my great fore-paws stretched out before me, dozing, full-bellied. Rousing at evening from my lair, and occasionally pausing to sleek my tawny flanks, I prowled the ndian jungles in quest of sambhur, defeated any rival tigers who encroached on my territory, or occasionally took time off for a change of sex and the production of two handsome cubs. During lessons I lay a captive in a dark oppressive cage, gazing out proudly over the heads of my savage captors. At night, as I slaked my thirst, and perforce, cleaned my teeth, at the waterhole on the edge of the jungle, I could hear the dry grass rustle as the jackals, thinking I had grown old and feeble, closed in on me. In this fierce dream a governess who made emotional demands upon one ceased to exist. No one makes emotional demands upon tigers, or, if they do, they go away empty.

Also unsympathetic to this way of life was Mademoiselle Matthéi, who came on Tuesdays and Thursdays to teach me French, and has permanently given those two days an unpopular saxe-blue colour. Mademoiselle Matthéi had saxe-blue eyes, walked with what seemed to me a mincing gait, and wore a high net collar supported by little bones and trimmed with saxe-blue velvet bows. She would cry, 'Oh! Priskilla! Oh, oh, Priskilla!' throwing her hands in the air over my *dictées*, and was, all in all, no fit companion for one of the larger fauna. My tail lashed contemptuously, and I moved uneasily in the heavy chains that my Indian captors had put upon me. '*Attention, Priskilla! Faites attention, s'il vous plaît. On ne dit pas* ou, *comme ça, on dit* u, u, U.' My great golden eyes narrowed dangerously. Soon my teeth would meet in the backbone of a wild sambhur with a delicious and ferocious crunch.

In the outside world things also were less happy and more restless. My father did not seem any longer to go off duck-shooting at El Fayum. One of Mohammed's twins had died the boy, the one that mattered to him. He was getting on in years; in his face could be read the sorrowful thought that this might be his last son. Lord Allenby and Mr Horan had both lost their only sons in the war, which only seemed to make them even nicer to other people's children, and not like some people, less nice. Both of them had, in very different ways, that quality that has no name but which imparts the certainty that whichever side they are on is bound to win.

Peace, as ever, produced a sharp outbreak of nationalistic fervour, as if, attuned to war, people were unable to stop. This came to a head in a pitched battle at the Sporting Club. (Why pitched? Something, no doubt, to do with cricket.) All the English boys, already delayed by the war, had been swept away wholesale to their prep-schools in England. Championed only by male characters of seven years old and under, we felt like Roman Britain after the recall of the legions to Rome. In these circumstances power passed easily into the hands of the French. Everyone at the Sporting Club now tended to be English or French; these, as one grew older, were the only socially acceptable things to be. The Greeks and Cypriots and Maltese were English, the Syrians, some of the Turks, and some of the Egyptians were French. We fell, muttering indignantly, under the tyrannical rule of Max Harari, a relation of Ferdinand de Lesseps and sustained by a doughty bodyguard of henchmen one of whom was a wiry girl called Yvonne who had reached the staggering age of fourteen and had plaits looped up at the ends. Max too was nearly fourteen, and seemed a great Tiberius Caesar of a boy, arrogant and domineering and wearing those very short French shorts which mysteriously exacerbate the English, who invented shorts and feel sure that they know the right place to stop.

It became clear that something had to be done. There were a number of English, but they were all rather young and small. An army was assembled and hastily put through its paces. Nervous but determined, it issued a challenge for three o'clock on the following day on the cricket ground.

Very fortunately, it was Miss G.'s day off. Annie Mac-Nichol, sweet and unsuspecting, could be relied upon not to interfere. The Russells' old Nanny, scenting danger like a warhorse, had taken Camilla and John away for a long safe walk on the far side of the island. The British army, as so often in history, was under Anglo-Irish command, the general in this case being Judy McLaughlin, a determined in-fighter with a starched yellow piqué dress and tight auburn plaits. I had gloriously reached the rank of major, now that so many majors had gone off to their prep-schools, but there were, besides Judy, two lieutenant-colonels over my head. As always in amateur armies there was that difficulty over the refusal of the younger members to be private soldiers. Alethea, the youngest in the army and owing her position to influence (mine), was a corporal, as also were Wilfred and Dorian Russell and the Westropp twins.

We crouched in ambush behind the bowling screen as the

hour of battle approached, our hearts whirring like refrigerators. The minute hand in the clock above the cricket pavilion crept slowly higher. From the polo ground came the familiar crack and knock of our older compatriots playing polo in their carefree adult way. A donkey brayed distantly with its sad sobbing cry from the direction of the Pongly-Zongly bridge. The tops of the palm trees in the Swings stirred faintly, giant feather dusters reaching into the high blue sky. Kites and crows wheeled and skirmished overhead. The suffragis in the club house were beginning to clatter the tea-cups. It was almost three. Max Harari and his army appeared suddenly from under the mulberry trees along the edge of the Swings and advanced across the cricket ground in careless open array.

It is a mistake to set upon a proud adversary in a manner that suggests that he is of no account, as the French found at Agincourt, as the English found at Bunker Hill. The English army swept out from behind the bowling screen with desperate purpose, fell upon the French, and after a short sharp affray in which no quarter was given or asked, laid them low. No weapons were employed; it was a case of hands, legs, and morale. Those above the rank of captain sat on the chests of the French; lower ranks were allowed to pin their outer limbs to the ground. Even Max Harari was unable to move; Denis Molesworth sat on his stomach; the red plaits of Judy whipped scornfully across his face. His legs were entirely covered by lance-corporals in embroidered linen. Jennifer Trelawney, with Cornish doggedness, pinned one arm; a skirmish of Selbys sat on the other. Torture was not applied; not from any lack of ill-will, but because none of us knew how, though Rennie Maudslay, a cocky four-year-old with drooping eye-lids, had to be restrained from dancing on the fallen foe. We sat there heavily and remorselessly until the French were forced to admit, through clenched teeth, that the English were best. It was a moment of huge satisfaction, and all knowledge of it was, by general consent, withheld from our parents.

This success made everyone rather less than kind to the children of the Milner Commission, who visited Egypt this winter with a view to recommending a reformed constitution. Defeating one Swings tyranny, we replaced it with another, a tight Anglo-Saxon oligarchy. The mantle of Max Harari fell easily upon our shoulders. One of the Milner Commission's children was a red-haired boy called George Nathaniel, who openly boasted that he was a godson of George Nathaniel Curzon. This piece of side was treated in a summary manner. The children of the Milner Commission seemed to be made of thin stuff, and even declined to drink cups of tea into which a fly had fallen and been whisked out. 'You seem to think', George Nathaniel complained, 'that you are Kings and Queens of the Sporting Club.' 'Of *course,*' we told him, with delighted arrogance, 'we *are*. You are just tourists. You can't talk Arabic and you are afraid of flies.'

Things softened down in the way that they do over Christmas. Miss G. gave me such a handsome present that I felt ashamed of my behaviour to her, and stopped being The Tiger for a spell of days. She was reading us *The Cloister and the Hearth*, and I fell soothingly in love with Gerard, its very unfortunate hero. He, Sir Lamorak de Galis, and Owen Wister's Virginian, along with several flesh and blood characters, shared my affections this winter in those brief intervals when I assumed human form. Perhaps Miss G., too, became easier; it may be that my mother's efforts to find friends and amusements for her were bearing fruit. For me, she had no reality but as an obstacle; never did it occur to me that she could be a human being with feelings and fears and hopes of her own. 'Forgive us our trespasses,' I prayed comfortably into Annie MacNichol's confiding lap. Miss G.'s trespasses, of course, came into quite another category. She was not a person. But for the moment the winds of rage were lulled. Miss G. seemed to have given up the project of being loved for herself. She gave me several more small brass pyramids, as an explorer might propitiate the savage and recalcitrant chieftain of a strange island.

The garden was a solace and I had some sweeping agricultural plans. Egypt was a supreme country, but it lacked woodlands, and this deficiency I proposed to remedy. With a little care and forethought, one could arrange a counterpart to the Devon beechwoods. I began on the establishment of a forest. It meant sacrificing the violet bed; but what are violets when a mighty forest is at stake? There were violets in other parts of the garden. I extended my territory along towards the potting-shed, and planted a bohinnia, two eucalyptus trees, a jacaranda, and a rubber tree. These would form shade for the beeches and oaks to get going in. On the other side of the path

I laid out a small but sufficient apricot grove. The whole site was only about thirty feet by twelve, but everything has to start somewhere, and I felt no doubt that many a mighty forest had begun from less. One day a deep rich woodland would cover the whole of Gezira. There would be rock pools, boulders, waterfalls, moss, ferns, primroses, pink campions and bluebells. Independent Egyptians, sitting under its grateful shade with their feet in the stream, would bless the name of Priscilla Hayter, if indeed any of them were able to pronounce it. The trees, enthusiastically visited every morning, flourished; and seemed almost to grow as one watched them. 'Those apricot trees', my mother pointed out, 'are much too near the house. They'll never root properly.' But I lived in a steady hope that the laws of nature would be in so good a cause conveniently suspended.

She was reading me *Barnaby Rudge,* which I secretly found uncongenial. Why were we not back in the middle of *Alfgar the Dane,* or *The Rival Heirs*? But parents, whatever their failures in judgement, had a kind of intrinsic perfection; they were beings beyond criticism; one rested in them. Why could not one always be with them? Why did they have other functions than parenthood, boring and distracting tasks like earning a living or administering a country or running the house? Why must they do the flowers in church, have Egyptian judges and their wives to dinner, visit people ill in hospitals? Why must they waste time talking to, being with, all those other grown-ups?

Mohammed had lit the wood fire, which crackled agreeably, and the curtains were drawn. The room was furnished in an uncompromisingly English manner, with a bright green carpet, a mahogany-framed looking-glass with a gold eagle over the fireplace, and Chelsea china figures reflecting themselves in it. There were leather-bound classics in a bookcase with Rockingham china in the upper part of it, a piano, a Chippendale bureau, Hepplewhite chairs, a table covered in illustrated books, and silver framed photographs of relations wearing either muslin or uniforms. Down each side of the fireplace were Victorian silhouettes, and miniatures of earlier days. Armchairs and sofas were covered in a white rose-patterned chintz with occasional bands of narrow green stripes. There were a number of small tables with silver lampstands whose shades were made of pleated silk trimmed with a frill. Not so much as a Benares brass tray or a pastel of an Egyptian village had been allowed to creep in. Persian rugs were different, they had, like oriental china, been introduced into English houses long enough ago to have acquired a kind of honorary Englishness. The walls were hung with water-colour sketches in gilt frames, of grassy English scenes and lush overhanging trees, painted by my father's aunts, who luckily were not without talent. One was of a road by a stone wall, with three figures walking away into the distance. I always imagined it to be a picture of Christ and the two disciples on the road to Emmaus, and was immensely surprised to find, when I grew tall enough to see it clearly, that it was unmistakably a piece of Kent, and to realise that there was only one man and that he was leading two horses.

'Priscilla darling, you are not following the story.'

'Yes, I am.'

'It's the end of the chapter anyway, so I won't start another. Would you like some ranunculus for your garden?'

'Well, perhaps. About two. And red ones. Not yellow. Hassan has given me some, you know, pink silk daisy plants with grey leaves full of juice like there are at Mena House.'

'Mesembryanthemum?'

'Yes,' I said, not risking it.

'Hassan', my father pointed out, 'has no business to present you with Egyptian government property. Try teaching him to say mesembryanthemum as a punishment.'

Happiness is dull and blissful and unhurried and consists of nothing much. From the hall too soon the hateful voice of Miss G. could be heard calling out that it was bedtime. Getting up slowly, I returned into my surly feline skin. It was Annie's task to see us to bed, where was she? Her day out; curse and bang it. The hall was large and high and cool, it was an open stretch of jungle, where the grass grew banister high. My tail flicked lightly against it as I passed, padding silently up the steep forest incline. Monkeys chattered at me from the trees above, but I ignored them; my only reply was a deep throaty growl and a silent lashing of my tail. The muscles rippled under the black stripes of my hide. 'Beddy-bies for sleepy heads,' Miss G. said.

In February my parents light-heartedly announced their intention of going with some friends on a trip up the Nile to

Luxor, Aswan, Abu Simbel, and other Nubian temples. I received this information in incredulous silence. The irresponsibility of parents is sometimes dumbfounding. They were leaving Alethea and me quite alone in the house with Miss G., Annie, Mohammed, and five other servants and going gallivanting off up the Nile without a care in their heads, acting indeed as if they had not, in their blindness, landed us in this governess impasse.

'I am writing a book,' I told my parents portentously, on the eve of their departure. My father had heard this one before.

'If you finish it,' he said, 'ten chapters and a proper ending, I will give you, let's see, what's next on the list, *Redgauntlet*.'

I held him to this, as we stood on the stone steps next morning, among the freesia pots, now in full bloom. 'If you have any doubts,' my mother told Miss G., 'ring up Dr Beddoes. Or Bonté Elgood.' And off they went, in quite obvious spirits, with scarcely a look back.

My book, needless to say, was about two happy carefree children, a girl and a boy, whose innocent lives were rendered insupportable to them by the introduction of an unkind Welsh governess who separated them from all their old and well-tried friends, banished the canary from their nightnursery, and taught them arithmetic by a particularly brutal and illogical method. Both these victims finally, broken-heartedly, in chapter eight, jumped into the Ganges. Their parents were left alone in the silent echoing house in Delhi. Gosh, where's the atlas? In the silent echoing house in Benares, repenting the day they had ever hit upon this ill-judged change of régime.

A part of me recognised this manoeuvre as paltry, mean, and exceedingly unlikely either to deceive or influence my parents. The other part pressed on in enjoyable self-righteousness. I had, after all, told them straight out that the arrangement would not do. If they knew all, they would not really want me to endure the emotional stress involved in keeping on terms with Miss G. How convince them, other than by these clumsy and roundabout methods? I left out the hairbrush incident, having the feeling that I did not come out of it too well. The happy innocent picture had a slight splodge on it at this point. There had been a moment when I had got hold of the hairbrush myself and – No, it was best forgotten.

'And so,' I wrote, pressing hard into the page, 'as night fell two hurrying figures might have been seen hastening to the river's brim.' It was very exciting, and I hurried with them. Soon the dark waters of the Ganges, or perhaps the turgid floods, would be closing over our heads. The pleasures of authorship closed over mine. Before long the remorseful parents, looking exactly like Colonel Blunt and Mrs Sharman, would be unavailingly pacing the banks of the mighty stream as it murmured, straggled? roared? What exactly *did* the Ganges do? *Rolled,* yes, emphatically that was best, rolled on its long course towards the vast reaches of the swelling Indian Ocean. Why swelling? Well, why not? The more swollen it was and the longer course of the mighty stream the more jolly sorry those parents would feel.

'Lunchies!' Miss G. called. 'Have you brushed your hair and washed your hands? No. I thought not. You're old enough now not to have to be told, surely? Iggeri, Iggeri!' Miss G. had learnt a few words of Arabic and used them continually to enforce her commands. 'Did I see you put out your tongue? Did I? Did I?'

People who do not feel rage can have no conception of how enjoyable it is. While it lasts rage is an intoxication like love, or drink, or music; a total freeing. One wants never to be out of it. The aftermath is terrible, the slow repentance, the patched-up goodwill, the uncertain rain-washed calm; but rage itself is an enviable state; one that leaves one all too soon. Let not the sun go down upon your wrath, Nanny frequently said, but it seemed impossible to. All too soon, generally in about twenty minutes, one was out the other side of it.

A few evenings after my father's return he handed my manuscript back to me in silence, accompanied by a copy of *Redgauntlet* in the beautiful blue-and-gold India paper edition which I was collecting. This absence of words was terrible to me. Condemnation, or faint praise, would have been infinitely better. In a flash of fury I threw my two exercise books into the fire.

'Not a bad idea,' my father commented.

'Oh darling, don't do that,' my mother said equably. 'All that wodgy paper. You'll put the fire out.'

It was probably not the difficulty of life with Miss G. that now caused Annie to leave us, but I blamed it on her all the same. It was more likely that the task of looking after two little girls who were already well cared-for offered not enough scope for the energies of her heart. She went away to nurse Egyptians in a fever hospital, where she presently got fever herself, and died. This, strangely, seemed not shocking but somehow right, as if Annie had arrived at a point in life where she could go no further, and so had to proceed elsewhere. Of all the deaths I had known this was the saddest, and the least jarring. She was succeeded by Rose Hunt, who was kindly enough, but quite another character; older, less outgoing. She sewed indefatigably most of the time, and was also my mother's maid, and began, disconcertingly, to call me Miss Priscilla, like maids did in England. She was peaceful and kind to be with, all the same.

As I went into the smoking-room one evening to sharpen a pencil, my father looked up from his desk and told me to come and see what he was doing. 'You won't often see this. I am writing out a cheque for four million pounds.'

I looked. The noughts meant nothing to me. I was still a mathematical moron. My father leant back in his chair. The hair round his temples was grey, but the top part was still light brown and slightly curly. His face was very brown, and to me looked exactly as a father's face should look. He had those slightly droopy moustaches which today seem unsympathetic and connected with Saxon invaders and Low's Colonel Blimp. His eyes were of a very definite, almost harsh blue. He had a beak nose and a firm jaw and laugh creases round his eyes. I thought him perfection, although not, at that moment, in a mood to be asked to sharpen my pencil. It was a relationship that was to remain crystallized in time; not subject to the strains of adolescence, to the rebellions of the twenties, to the rueful acceptance of the thirties, to the bored compassion of later years; an affection that the powerful hand of death would shortly render unbreakable.

'It's the winding-up', he said, 'of the Cotton Control Commission, which we set up in the war to prevent the fellaheen being swindled by rogues of contractors into selling their cotton for a quarter of its worth. I'm the chairman and I'm paying the money back to the Egyptian people.'

'What will they do with it?'

'That', my father said, 'is largely up to them. Move your elbow off the blotting paper.'

'If I was them I should buy a forest.'

'I think', he said, 'there may be some other things they want first. Perhaps no people can ever tell what any other people want first, only what *they* think they ought to want first. What we think people ought to want first is good government and internal peace, but it isn't always.'

'There is no legal thing,' he went on, 'nothing, to prevent me as chairman from taking ten per cent of this four million pounds. It was drawn up by . . . Pasha in a peculiar way while I was away and when he thought he was going to be chairman himself and that independence might arrive in time for him to cash in. Four hundred thousand pounds, for the taking. Shall we take it?'

'Gosh! Yes.'

'Yes,' he said, 'that's the principle on which this country

has always been run. These are the hardest working peasants in the world, squeezed dry down the millenniums for the benefit of a few rulers, with officials, often foreign, taking handsome pickings all the way. Egypt under the Khedives was known as the milch-cow of Europe, and the milkers were many and very expert. Why should we, the interfering English, upset the pattern of so many thousand years, with our cranky alien notions about justice and fair play and this and that, preaching a way of life that's quite incomprehensible to the whole groaning, grasping Middle East? Why don't we take our squeeze? Half the people think we do anyway, or think we're insane not to.'

'Why?' I said, intermittently following his line of thought.

'If we took it, of course we could never go back to England, and no one English would ever speak to us again. Or not to me. But we could buy a villa on the Golden Horn, or perhaps at Yalta. No, not Yalta; I'd forgotten, the Bolsheviks are there now. Or at Trebizond, with a garden full of terraces and cypress trees and jasmine. We could hear the fountains splash all night, and live in ease and comfort, waited upon by tireless Circassians with an eye to the main chance. It would be safety, for you, and your children and grandchildren, and all the joys of money, and they are real ones. Wealth is wealth, and people soon forget to ask where it comes from.'

We contemplated this prospect in silence for some moments, before I gave the right answer, mostly for the wrong reasons. I had formed the conclusion that life in England tended to be fun. A merry life of unarmed combat such as I envisaged could surely best be lived amongst the English, a people over against whom all others seemed in some unspecified way flimsy.

'And anyway,' I concluded, 'could we be sure that Charlie Chaplin films would come to Trebizond?'

He laughed, and the dream dissolved. But had there been a note of disappointment in his laughter? Had I somewhere failed to understand what he was driving at, what he wanted me to say? He went on writing his cheque and I went on doing my prep and the crickets went on shrilling outside in the black night. From the outer hall came the sounds of Mademoiselle Matthéi arriving to give me a lesson and being welcomed by Mohammed. The French are too much with us, late and soon.

Life jogged on; not smoothly, but in a series of hiccups. Towards the beginning of March Miss G. and I had a reverberating fracas about the decimal system, and next day she gave me a donkey cloth with ancient Egyptians on it, which I thought perfectly beautiful but not to the point. The khamseens were beginning, often the skies were dark with swirling sand. The Milner Commission had issued its report, which at any rate was polite about Egyptian aspirations, and did not brush them aside, but which in fact envisaged a veiled continuation of the British Protectorate for an indefinite time. To the Egyptian people it felt like the same old firman, the Turkish edict of the Ottoman Empire, not to be argued with, a direction issued from a remote capital. No Egyptian minister could be found to accept or negotiate on it. The cries for

stiklal el tam rose louder: Complete Independence! Kicking
he nursery table in a maddening manner during lesson time,
heartily concurred. What does it matter what other people
hink good for us, we have to be ourselves. *Istiklal el tam!* I
ashed out with unusual vigour and upset the bowl of sweet-
peas and everyone, including me, got very wet.

Someone in Egypt liked the Milner Report. On his way
back from the Ministry of Finance my father met a man with
a bundle of sugar cane on his back who was shouting, 'I am
contented; by God the Exalted, I am completely contented.'

'Why are you so contented, brother?' my father asked.

'Because of this Report.'

'Do you think it is a good scheme?'

'Do I know whether it is good or not?' the man with the
sugar cane said. 'I am like one of the cattle, and understand
none of these things. But they tell me that there will be an
agreement, and an end of all these quarrels and shootings;
and so I am contented. By God the Exalted; I am exceedingly
contented.

XIX

It was always as well to be through the Straits of Messina, where Scylla and Charybdis might still lean from their strongholds and get us. The glass Mediterranean spread smoothly before us, and the French liner, the *Lotus,* drove through it with the level certainty of a railway train; the bow wave fell cool and shining, the wake stretched far and straight behind us. In the bright rays of early morning the decks gave off a new-washed smell; the French, skilfully, seemed to use a soap for it less astringently carbolic than the one employed by the P. & O. There were no longer any drifting mines, and we were accompanied back to England this spring by my father, with his confident ability as a traveller and his easy flow of languages. In the dining saloon there were French breakfasts of croissants and cherry jam eaten amidst the deliciously powerful smell of French coffee. Perhaps after all, the French could be come to terms with, had their role in life? The glitter of the sea was dazzling; islands, those mysterious drowned mountains, rose up out of it all round in the vagueness of the horizon. In the smoking saloon, my father, with his strange pedantic notion that foreigners were human beings, was raconting and being raconted to by some Frenchmen, by an Italian with a blue chin, a Dane, and two Greeks with bulging waistcoats and heavy impressive jowls. From there he emerged, smoking a cigar, and divulged interesting information about lava in answer to questions as we passed the island volcano of Stromboli. How beautiful and unaccountable peace was – the haze on the horizon, the mirror sea, the absence of continual life-boat drill, the plentiful food in the dining saloon, the presence of both one's parents, and all about, floating in a dreamy way, the blue mountainous outlines of the Lipari islands. On the lee side of the ship my mother sat in a deck chair, Englishly doing her embroidery off a small folding table carried with us for that purpose. (We once arrived at Port Said with forty-two packages, as in *The Hunting of the Snark*.) 'Darling, I wonder if you would find my long-distance glasses, from the cabin?' In the cabin Rose Hunt was shaking out thick woolly jerseys, ready for England. Everything seemed, for a mirage moment, settled and stable and everlasting. 'If you've left your jacket on deck,' Rose said, 'you'd do well to bring it down here to me. I don't like the looks of some I see about.'

England itself, once reached, seemed less storm-battered. Even the derision of Hamer was less thundery and more jovial, and he was prepared now to show one his birds' egg collection. Those of one's uncles who had survived the war had bought themselves new motor-cars, Delages and Sunbeams, and drove about in them for fun, along the crown of the empty roads, allowing one to stop and pick foxgloves, and proudly blowing rubber horns.

'Don't do that, Andrew, you'll frighten the horses.'

'Nonsense, Meg, there are no horses.'

Nor were there. Carriages mouldered sadly in coach-houses, the harness of governess carts hung unpolished. Coachmen died of old age, and grooms were dispiritedly digging in the kitchen garden. People talked mockingly about profiteers, who were depicted in *Punch* wearing fur-collared coats, and spats on the wrong occasions, and smoking very large cigars, making disagreeable or ignorant remarks in strong cockney accents. There was still margarine at times when there should have been butter, and when one proudly bought a small doll for a shilling at the village shop everyone said, 'Gracious! A shilling for that! Why, before the war it would have been threepence halfpenny.'

In May my father left on a mission to Constantinople, which no one in the west had yet agreed to call Istanbul, in order to try and extract from the Khedive Abbas Hilmy as much as possible of the several million pounds belonging to the Egyptian State, which that light-hearted monarch had precautiously removed with him to Turkey in the summer of 1914. The Khedive, who was leading an agreeable life, was extremely loath to part; I do not know how the mission succeeded, but in any case it was prolonged. The battleship *Iron Duke* was at Constantinople, with Admiral de Robeck, who was a friend of my father's; and so, oddly, was my future husband, then a midshipman. There were present also a great many charming White Russian refugees, and a rollicking time was had by all, including, no doubt, the Khedive Abbas Hilmy.

My father returned to Cairo with or without several million

pounds, we shall never know, and came home on leave in July with Allenby, now High Commissioner in Egypt in succession to Wingate. In Allenby he found a boss under whom it was a delight, despite the increasing darkness of the scene, to work, and this regard seems to have been mutual. 'I have lost a dear friend,' Allenby wrote, when my father died. 'To no man do I owe a greater debt of gratitude. Through all the stormiest days in Egypt he was a loyal supporter and a sure guide on whom I could rely. Honoured and respected by all who knew him, British and Egyptian, he leaves a proud record.' And to my father when he left Egypt mortally ill (although neither of them knew this) in 1924, he wrote, 'I can only tell you that whatever good has been achieved during the last five years in Egypt has been in great measure due to you. Your ready co-operation and your wise counsels have been invaluable to me, and to part with you was a sore trial.'

In August my father was knighted. He was pleased to get it, specially on the recommendation of such a man as Allenby, as who is not, secretly or otherwise? So were we all, once Alethea had been assured that he would not immediately put on a suit of armour and leave home for ever on a very capacious horse in search of the Holy Grail. He went to see his father, now very old and grim, to tell him about his knighthood, and was roundly put down; my grandfather firmly asserting that it was a perfect waste of time to be made anything less than an earl.

Embarked just now upon a course of high-flown and high-minded literature, when the news came that one of my father's younger sisters, who had been a helpless invalid for many years, was unconscious and dying, I looked for an adequate display of noble emotions. My father had always been very fond of her and had spent much time sitting with her; here was his chance.

'Isn't it,' I asked, echoing the sentiments I had heard expressed in the kitchen, and wanting to splash about in them, if possible even more loudly, 'isn't it dreadful? Isn't it, Father, dreadfully sad about Aunt Phoebe? Isn't it most awfully sad that she is dying?'

'No,' my father said crisply. 'Best thing that could possibly happen to her.' And he continued to read the foreign news out of *The Times*. This came as a great surprise. Should he not have gone pale, dashed aside a manly tear, and strode from the room? How sadly does life fall away from literature. I was obliged to restore my shaken morale by a long close look at a bullfinches' nest, even though they had long since flown. Even at the funeral he declined to weep, or talk in a different voice. Yet even Rose Hunt, whose sister it wasn't, preserved for some days a hushed demeanour; and in the kitchen they had heaved and gulped all day – 'And she lying there so helpless with always a sweet smile on her face for everyone . . .' I would have liked to heave and gulp myself all day; they obviously got so much pleasure out of it. Yet what my father did must be right. Life was very confusing, and I added to its confusion by being as much shocked when my father failed to weep for his sister as I had been when my mother wept so openly for Uncle Harold. Parents can never hope to get it right, and do well to go their own way.

In the summer holidays the ploys arranged by our parents no longer seemed so infallibly right and enjoyable as they once did. There was, for instance, a family tennis tournament; the aunts thought it would be nice. Here I suffered sharp reverse, being beaten in a single by Harry who was younger and had only started to play tennis that summer. He stood surrounded by the plaudits of the crowd. His face creased suddenly into an enormous grin, he shook silently all over with mocking and triumphant laughter. His mouth looked as if it might meet behind. I went furiously away to look for a lost ball in the macrocarpa, and here, never a good loser, I dissolved into a rain of enraged tears. Harry, basically kind-hearted, came to assist, and I muttered over a shoulder that I had found the ball and was just coming. It soon became impossible to emerge, with signs of such unworthy emotion on my face; I stayed gloweringly in this scratchy green sanctuary whilst everyone else went in to tea. From this impasse I was rescued by my father, who, accustomed to analogous situations amongst Egyptian officials, had no difficulty in coaxing me back into a sufficient self-esteem. I went with him meekly past the stream and the raspberry canes and the small green apples ripening on the trees. On the way up to the house he gave me a bar of chocolate and urged me, in mild terms, not to be so bloody silly.

Hardly was this over before the holidays were further darkened by the production of a fairy play. The dress rehearsal seemed in a way quite gay, but when the day came and the audience arrived, melancholy prevailed. A born non-actress, obliged to take the part of the Good Fairy (which as a piece of type-casting could hardly have been more inept), dressed in pale blue satin and diamanté, I bumbled through the few lines of whimsy benevolence which the part demanded, only occasionally able to whip a heavy scowl of embarrassment off my face. Waving my wand, I even executed a fairy dance, which must have looked more like a foal let out into a field than anything else. The kindly audience, which consisted mainly of Rose Hunt and her cronies, applauded encouragingly, but could not compensate for the expressions of Hamer and Harry, who, seated cross-legged in the front row, made mocking faces. My sufferings were as nothing compared to those of William, a born non-actor and compelled on a warm summer afternoon to don chain armour and a helmet and be a romantic prince, his face set in stony disdain. This infant martyrdom was imposed on us in the interests of the producer, an aunt who was saddened by the death of the invalid sister and was thought by my parents to need taking out of herself. Alethea, it is pleasant to record, had a lively part as the maid and enjoyed the play. It was a disappointing summer holiday and the thought of Miss G.'s return from Ireland hung like a shade over it. The point, however, was taken by our parents, and we spent the next summer holiday entirely in boats.

The summer, in spite of a railway strike, ended in a blaze of glory. It was made clear to us that Miss G. was not coming back; we sailed for Egypt without her. The ship was not large enough to contain my joy, its decks thundered ceaselessly under racing feet as the promontories of Italy rolled past and the sun grew higher and warmer every day. Arrived at Alexandria, I laid myself out in a basket chair in the hotel garden and let the sun soak in, clapping my hands and causing several grown men to come running with glasses of iced orangeade, thus setting up a wave of feeling that it was as well I was going away to school in the spring. The sun soaked through me to the very backbone. My toes, in the freedom of sandals, spread and wriggled luxuriously in the baking light. A solitary noonday cricket started up in the oleanders. Dragonflies, green gauze biplanes, zigzagged amongst the aromatic shrubs of the hotel garden. Glorious, sumptuous, governess-free Egypt, held in fee by me, by me, by me. Blue-tailed lizards slid under the basketwork chaise-longue. Soused in pleasurable hubris, I clapped my hands for yet another iced orangeade. 'Dear,' my mother said, 'I think–' but it was time to catch the train for Cairo.

At the station a beggar was shuffling along outside the railings, but I looked on him now with a glassier eye. 'Al Allah,' I said, carelessly consigning him to the care of God. Had the plight of the more luckless Egyptians become all this while less piteous, or one's own heart harder? To grow up among poverty so vast and irremediable is an experience to scar a lot of the sensitivity out of one; and what constantly disconcerts the warmth of humanitarianism is the frequent refusal of those in misery to *be* miserable. The loud resilient laughter and enjoyment of the very poor wells up like a fountain, to baffle and confound sympathy. Real despair, faces and bearing truly without hope, arc far more often to be seen in a bang-up midland New Town on an income of £30 a week. But what conclusion we draw from these observable facts is another thing.

There was great comfort in being back with Miss Quibell, that composed and undemanding intelligence. Mary Rowlatt and I, now the oldest in the school, stayed on in grown-up grandeur for forty minutes after everyone else had left, sitting through the hot noons doing advanced subjects like Amenhotep IV and the rivers of China. I was quicker, and Mary more thoughtful; Miss Quibell treated us both with impartial firmness and encouragement. She praised Mary's sketch maps, and gently persuaded me to shorten my long turgid essays about the Yellow River. Sometimes she wrote V.G., in her neat round hand, and one felt it was V.G. indeed. She led me with calm slowness through the mazes of arithmetic. Guilt fell away; an easy docility settled upon me, at least in lesson times. Walking home with Rose Hunt I no longer kicked up the clouds of dust, or whacked my hoopstick along the fields of sugar-cane. I took up carpentry and watercolour sketching, and stamp collecting and embroidery, and may even have seemed, for a time, almost civilized.

Just before Christmas there was to be a dance. My mother had a niece staying for this winter, the dance was for her, and Alethea and I were to be allowed to stay up for the first part. Not Kitty and Lydia Bennet, rolled into one and multiplied by ten, could have looked forward to this more excitedly than Alethea and I did. Every plan connected with it was magical and fascinating; the music, the displacement of the furniture, the invitations, the supper, the decorations. My mother was making us new dresses for it, of embroidered net; Rose was making the pink satin underskirts. 'The band will play in the corner by the piano,' we told each other, over and over again, like an incantation, 'and people will sit out in the smoking-room, and *both* halls, and the verandah.' To sit out, how sophisticated it sounded. It meant, we knew, leaning back, and smoking cigarettes, and showing off in a way that people did not ordinarily bother about, and talking, in a particular high, airy sort of voice. What did grown-ups so endlessly manage to talk *about*? The verandah was going to have carpets for the occasion, and ashtrays, and cigarette boxes on little tables, and one or two other neighbouring suffragis, summoned by Mohammed, were coming in to help.

It was an entrancing prospect that was never to be subjected to the danger of falling flat. Everyone, starting with Alethea and ending with my father, caught whooping cough, by the time we had all finished it would be Lent, when, of course, to dance was unthinkable. Although when Lent came the niece did in fact continue to dance, at the Semiramis Hotel. Times were changed.

'Next winter,' my mother promised, but then she remembered that next winter I would be away at school in England, learning Algebra and Latin, and it was hoped, how to live and let live.

Poor Alethea became the subject of some sharp reproaches.

'I never catch things. It was you that started chicken-pox as well. Why didn't you see that nun and all those little children coming, at the Grotto? Why did you *let* them cough all over you?'

'A cat can cough at a king,' Alethea said, between her whoops, but the logic of this failed to penetrate my indignation.

Out of quarantine we were joined at school by a new arrival, Helen Gary, daughter of the American consul. This was a new phenomenon in life, the All-American child, never before encountered outside the pages of Mark Twain or Louisa M. Alcott, and expected, therefore, if a boy to be all right, but if a girl to be pretty soppy. We regarded her with critical interest. She was far from soppy, and seemed friendly. She spoke English, albeit with a strong Devon accent, but appeared to have been badly deprived in the field of education. She knew nothing of Canute, William the Conqueror, Coeur-de-Lion, or the little princes in the Tower. Neither Bloody Mary, Oliver Cromwell, nor Admiral Nelson had ever come her way. Odder still, she seemed not to have been let in on Socrates or Julius Caesar or Yenghiz Khan or Marco Polo, hitherto believed to be universal possessions. They had even rushed the poor girl through the only interesting part of her own history, the Red Indian part, and fobbed her off with a lot of boring Presidents in black frock coats. How strange it was to have such a very unglittering world picture! They had also filled her up with a lot of inaccurate information about the English, leading her to suppose that the War of American Independence was a real war, and not just a piece of badly handled colonial trouble complicating the real war with France. It was rum. And to imagine there'd been another one, that time in 1812 when America had tried to bag Canada and it hadn't come off. People who had not been, as we had, principally engaged for 600 years in fighting the French or Germans, simply did not know what war was. Helen Gary even, amazingly, announced that the Americans had won the Great War. This could not be allowed to pass.

'There wouldn't,' I concluded sternly, 'have been an America if it hadn't been for England.' I was sitting on the Westropps' swing and gave it a mighty push to emphasize the point.

'Yes, there would then,' Helen Gary stoutly maintained, turning her head from side to side to fix me with her eye as I flew past her on the swing. 'We would have been something else, Italian, like Christopher Columbus, or something.'

'Italian! Golly! You'd all have been scalped if you'd been Italian. You had to be English to do the difficult part.'

Helen was undefeated, but when she drew breath I came off the swing and went on to tell her that I had seen (how?) a plan of the armies on the Western Front in 1918, German divisions massed against the British, thin against the French divisions, and strung out contemptuously against the Americans.

'Well, the Germans lost, anyway, didn't they?' Helen Gary said unanswerably. I meditated pushing her into Sir William Willcocks's verbena border, but he could be seen approaching, with his sober gait and his panama hat. Besides, she was larger, older, heavier, and really rather nice.

All the same it was strange that someone speaking the same tongue should have such a very odd world picture. Europe, as everyone knew, was an exclusive Sporting Club, in which the rest of the world was simply not allowed to play, occupied as it continuously was by really important fixtures, Greece *v.* Persia, Rome *v.* Carthage, Christendom *v.* Islam, Austria *v.* Italy, Spain *v.* Germany, Russia *v.* Poland, and the perennial match of England *v.* France. As a great treat America had been, in the Great War, allowed to play on the centre court, but could not, of course, as yet hope to qualify for the finals. These basic facts of life Helen had somehow failed to grasp. She did not stay at Miss Quibell's for very long; perhaps her mother feared she might become imbued with colonialism, or simply felt that life was too short to spend catching up on Romulus and Remus and all those columns of pounds, shillings and pence.

There was still the Gezira Sporting Club at which to throw my small but efficient spanner into the comity of nations. Nothing makes the average sensual character more fiercely chauvinistic than an upbringing in an international society, and parents wishing their children to grow up with a world outlook should keep them in their native land until they are at least twenty, and carefully supervise their reading matter. But there are some rare people who are by their natures proof against the temptations of race. Mary Rowlatt was such a one. It was she who used to restrain me at the Sporting Club from addressing my playmates in derogatory phrases culled from the pages of Sir Walter Scott.

'Leave go, leave go, you carrion crow,' I would exclaim to a Syrian boy with whom I was disputing the roof of the summerhouse at the Swings. 'Leave go, Dog of an Infidel!'

'No!' Mary would counter, her large eyes flashing, her narrow charming face crimson with embarrassment and indignation. 'He's not an infidel! He's no more an infidel than you are, he's a Copt.'

I was impressed by the justice of this, and by the fervour with which it was announced. I would give ground and descend, like the bully in *Tom Brown's Schooldays*; sloping off as good as pussy to climb the mulberry trees. The ripe fruit fell squashily from the shaken boughs; it is unfortunate that mulberries, looking so beautiful, should taste so sour and drear. It also seemed a pity, at the time, that none of them fell squashily upon the Syrian, upon his look of triumph and his neat white shirt.

Somewhere in the air the thought of school in England hung, obtruding itself between the bright days and the evenings beside the crisp log fire. Part of me wanted it; needed the harder lessons, the faster runners, a world of bigger and better Joneses with whom to keep up. Part of me wanted very much to come to grips with the larger, tougher, grown-up world of England. Part of me wanted complete independence. A very small part of me knew that an added stringency was necessary, that I had grown out of this Eden and indeed was all set to become its serpent. And a larger part longed, like the man with the load of sugar cane on his back, to remain for ever the irresponsible child of loving parents, doing as I liked and receiving the forgiveness and acceptance that came to me as their child; living out my life in this idyllic sun-spattered land, seeing the Nile rise and fall, seeing the Pyramids stand in the glow of morning, feeding silkworms and canaries and rabbits, playing easy imaginary games with Alethea, watching the growth of my forest. A kind of enchanted sadness hung over everything, aggravated no doubt by post whooping-cough depression.

Such thoughts did not for long occupy my mind, except in church, where one is obliged to sit still and face reality, to cogitate upon good and evil,' The face and voice of Mr Horan, now more lined than ever, adjured one to thoughtfulness and, briefly, inclined one to goodness. 'Beloved let us love one another,' Allenby read, from behind the eagle lectern, 'for love is of God, and every one that loveth is born of God, and knoweth God.' His voice was calm, unselfconscious, and certain. The words, needing no reinforcement, were, to a childish ear, reinforced by their emanation from the mouth of so towering a personality. 'He that loveth not knoweth not God,' Allenby continued, in even tones, and somewhere within me something was saying what a pity it was still to be wearing a white jersey and a white skirt on Sundays when other and younger children wore green or pink or blue. 'He that dwelleth in love dwelleth in God, and God in him,' Allenby said, turning the page. Whether next year one's mother would allow one a green coat? Downe House, splendidly, wore purple coats, like Dives, who was clothed in purple and fine linen. Dives had had to answer for it later on, owing to not being kind to Lazarus. Could one not wear purple *and* be kind to Lazarus? Or *be* Dives, and jolly well have the fun of it while it lasted? But then there was that awful thirstiness, and I knew what thirst was like, the desert parching of the mouth that made one unable to think about anything else but water. Downe House wore purple coats and I could hardly wait to get into one. I looked down scornfully at the sleeve of my unbearably babyish white jacket. 'There is no fear in love,' Allenby read; but it was all very well for him, not afraid of Turks and not afraid of being thought feeble by the home government for his humanity to Egyptians, and not afraid of being thought a tyrant by the Egyptians for his firmness with them. Some people, I grumbled to myself, do not fear anyway. Some people are born good. Some people don't even have to try. How can anybody talk about equality when some people are born enemies and some people are born friends, some lovers and some haters? Some people – An army of Joneses, effortlessly virtuous, tramped maddeningly through the landscape of my mind. 'If a man say, I love God, and hateth his brother, he is a liar,' Allenby pointed out, and I knew that he and St John were right, and opted out of this uncomfortable knowledge and stared mindlessly at the toes of my shoes and wanted church to be over. The Christian religion was much too difficult, and one had better paddle about the fringes and not attempt to dive in, unless one were St John or Allenby, or someone of a like calibre. Don't tell me, I urged some unseen mentor, about the forgiveness of sins, because although God doesn't get bored of forgiving, I get *jolly* bored of being forgiven, day in day out. I would like to be in a permanent state of *not having to be forgiven*. And yet, and yet. They were all so nice, and any mug could see they *were* the winning side, and I would like to be one. It was too difficult; and seemed to put paid to too great a quantity of lush activities, such as eating too much chocolate cake, and being beastly to Syrians.

You cannot opt out, you *are* one, the unseen mentor chipped in. You have signed on the dotted line, or they have for you; and this was at once glowing, and rather sad. One did not know whether to be glad or sorry, relieved or resentful. Allenby was taller than Kitchener, and twice the size of Sir Reginald Wingate; far more of him appeared above the lectern. In the army he had been called the Bull, but he did not sound like one now. He stepped down from behind the lectern and went majestically back to the front pew, and it was the Te Deum. But I was twelve now ; the cumulus clouds were battening down, and the legs of the cherubim and seraphim swung less zestfully in the ringing blue of the sky.

XX

Still faintly whooping, we visited Joseph's well, rock-hewn and bottomless, and the huge mosque at the Citadel, wandering through its cool spaces with the large yellow slippers put on to cover up our unhallowed Nazarene feet, slopping off behind us. Edgy and convalescent, we enjoyed this less than we might have done.

'Don't cough, B.,' I said, preachily; irritated by the noise it made in the high dim silence. 'It's a holy place. Shut up.'

'Shut up yourself. I know that as much as you. And anyway you haven't got your holy slippers on properly.'

'They're too big.'

'Mine are perfectly as big and I've got them on, jolly well.'

The roof seemed hugely high, and there was a delicious smell of incense, holiness, dust, and silence, and the rather less delicious tang given off by the Egyptian guide. Now that he had had said his say, the stillness was broken only by the flapping of our slippers.

It was a relief to get out into the bright sun.

'By all the laws of architecture,' my father said, 'those two minarets shouldn't stand up. It's like balancing two upright pencils. It shouldn't work. But there they are. Kept up apparently by faith.'

We went on to look, with fascinated pleasure, at the place where the last of the trapped Mameloukes had leapt his horse from the high walls. Mohammed Ali, early in the previous century, had lured the Mameloukes into the Citadel to a banquet, trapped them in a narrow alley, and murdered them all, except this solitary one. His horse was killed under him in the fall, but he himself had escaped.

'The poor horse,' Alethea said, Englishly, 'it was nothing to do with *it*, whatever the Mameloukes had done.' 'Who built the Citadel?' I asked, switching hastily from this sad thought.

'Saladin, originally. Yusef Saleh-ed-Din. The well is probably called after him. The walls and the fortress anyway, he built.'

Saladin. Saladin. The name had a beautiful echo, like Sir Lamorak de Galis. What fun to live in the Citadel, and look, from so high up, across Cairo and the river, with the Mocattam hills behind one, to the desert sweep to the westwards with the Pyramids standing up against the sky. I added Saladin to my collection of loved objects. It would have been fun to live in the Citadel, although the competition, amongst the wives, would have been intense. A mob of Joneses, with immense compelling oriental eyes, to keep up with.

'It was on this flat space that the Mameloukes used to play polo. They were superb horsemen, and rode very short, but it was pretty dangerous and they frequently got killed. There were hundreds of people watching, and whenever the Khalifa hit the ball all the people blew trumpets and banged drums. Cairo was bigger than London then, in the fifteenth century, bigger than Paris or Madrid, and much better lit.' Alethea and I contemplated this picture in silent pride, as though we had organized the whole thing ourselves.

Once more, accompanied by three other little girls, we did the round of the Rameseses in the Cairo Museum. 'May God have mercy on you,' the doorman said kindly to my father as we left, 'and send you a son.' 'I have one,' my father told him, making no attempt to explain the curious system by which English fathers send their only sons in early childhood three thousand miles away from them to school. 'Ah,' said the doorman, running his eye over the tally of little girls, 'God in the end is faithful and compassionate.'

Frequent as had been the picnics to the Pyramids, the bathes at Mena House, the camel rides around the Sphinx, Alethea and I had never yet achieved our long-held ambition of going to the top of the Great Pyramid. I had once, on one of many Nanny picnics in the ruined temple below the Second Pyramid, empty of life and strewn with broken pieces of granite and alabaster brought with such expense of human effort from who knew where, climbed some way up this one. My plan had been to get anyway as far as the shiny top of this pyramid, the only part of the three which is left unstripped of its granite covering. This dream had faded. Nanny, alas, saw me in time, when I felt myself to be agonisingly nearly there. Crimson and gesticulating, she stood in the ruined temple, making imperative movements suggesting descent. There was a certain degree of redness in Nanny's face that meant business, and was discernible even from three-quarters of the way up a pyramid. Coming down a pyramid is dull, and even, when you are seven, dangerous. You have to jump off each block, and your skirt sticks on it, and you nearly fall off the edge of the next block. 'You weren't even nearly there,' Nanny said crushingly, brushing the stony dust off me, and this may have been so; it is impossible, once on a pyramid, to judge how far up there is still to go. How galling it was, this inter-fering conspiracy of grown-ups to prevent children breaking their necks! How they gang up, and even expect one to be interested in their stuffy hobby! I knew very well that I would never now feel the shiny top of the Pyramid of Chephren. 'There now,' Nanny said, 'run about and play. Set so much as a foot on that pyramid again and I'll spifflicate you.'

My father, surprisingly, felt rather the same. He had a thing against going up, or inside, the Great Pyramid. I never knew why; he was not superstitious, nor was he afraid of heights. Perhaps he regarded the whole thing as a tourist-fleecing racket, and a waste of time. Edward Cecil had mockingly assured him that he had carved the name of Hayter in huge letters on the summit, hoping to tease my father into going up to see whether this horrifying outrage had indeed been done; but he never went. This winter, standing at the foot of the pyramids, we had seen a bulky and portentous-looking man striding up the hill from Mena, his coat-tails blowing back, his chin thrust out against the desert wind. 'Winston Church-ill,' my father said. He was the first person I had ever seen wearing dark glasses, then a novelty; they made him, I thought, look like the fish footman in *Alice*. I was so

preoccupied with the dark glasses that I failed to notice
T. E. Lawrence, who, unromantically wearing a dark blue suit,
accompanied Winston on this day. My father took me by the
shoulder and whisked us firmly round the corner of the pyramid, out of range. 'I spent', he said, 'the whole of yesterday
with Churchill in the role of a local expert; and I don't want
to spend the whole of this afternoon'; for Churchill, alas, was
not in those years liked by his contemporaries, especially those
with strong characters themselves. Nor was this wholly a shal-
lowness of opinion, for genius and greatness, in its rough road
to maturity, sometimes wears an awkward or conceited form.
He was thought to have done something faintly non-cricket in
South Africa, escaping from a prisoner-of-war camp in a way
that bogged the chances of everyone else, and was looked
upon with a mingling of derision and unwilling admiration
for the tenacity and cockiness with which he maintained his
often wrong-headed views. It was a failure in judgement for
which their sons were all to bleed.

My father was adamant about the Great Pyramid. It thus
fell to the lot of Sir Frederick Rowlatt to take charge of the
expedition to the top. We forgathered at the foot of the pyramid; Mary and Pamela Rowlatt neat in reefer jackets and
round panama hats, Alethea and I, dressed as usual rather
inconclusively. Rose Hunt was left knitting behind an
immense fallen piece of alabaster, occasionally saying, '*Imshi,
ya wallad*,' in rather a prim voice to inquisitive intruders. Our
hearts thumped wildly with anticipation, with the tremen-
dousness of this so long awaited moment. Up above us, the

angle of the pyramid stretched, an endless succession of yellow, yard-square stone blocks. I was allotted a very old Egyptian guide whom I was obliged to haul up the more difficult places, urging him on to a smarter pace in my kitchen Arabic; he imploring me to go slower and wait for him, in tones which became increasingly breathless. There are probably few things in nature more inexhaustibly energetic than a long-legged child of twelve who really wants to get somewhere. The last few steps before the top were almost unbearably exciting. Sir Frederick arrived last, slightly out of breath, but still with his habitual kindly dryness of manner. The name of Hayter was not, I was relieved to see, engraved upon the summit, but the name of Amos was; perhaps an early indiscretion of Sir Maurice's, or of his father's. A stiff wind blew, flapping the cotton skirts of our dresses and causing Sir Frederick to clutch on to his hat. 'Keep back', he said at intervals, and in unruffled tones, 'from the edge.'

The verdant valley of the Nile stretched out before us, narrow between its yellow desert hills, Cairo was a pile of white boxes, the minarets of the Citadel were matchsticks, the mosque a misty curve. The mud villages stood amongst palm groves, the water buffaloes waded in the flooded fields, the wheels of the saggias slowly turned. Almost one could see the camels and the donkeys and the little boys in long robes, and the fly-covered babies, swinging along on their mothers' shoulders. In imagination one could smell the harsh insistent smells and the fuel cakes of dried dung, could hear the flies buzzing, and the wind rattling the dry leaves of the palms, and the loud furious arguments in which every passion seems to be engaged but in fact all that is being said is, Will you milk the goat or shall I? I felt with a pang of grief that this was my country and that I could never leave it, or be at home elsewhere than here. The descent was slow and reluctant and slightly giddifying and our shoes got full of little stones.

'That wasn't very kind to Rose. After all, it is she who has the washing and mending of your stockings.'

White stockings. Insisted upon by the harsh and beautiful Swedish countess who taught us gym, then known as Swedish drill, near Kasr-el-Nil in Cairo, and with whom I was instantly at loggerheads amongst the ribstalls. White stockings which if put on too early, as Rose had insisted, rather naturally became covered in green amongst my now really prosperous forest, and involved one in reproaches.

'Don't you sometimes', my mother suggested, 'feel that you ride rather roughshod over people?'

I looked at my mother with incredulity. I was fond of Rose Hunt, but her preoccupation with the whiteness of my stockings was absurd.

'I know you don't mean it, but for the people whose feelings are hurt, it is just as bad as if you did.'

'They *will* be so irritating.'

'Almost everybody will be irritating,' my mother said, 'sooner or later. We have to live and let live.'

'Why can't Rose let me live with green stockings?'

'There's nothing to be gained by being rude and unkind to her. People all have feelings.'

Why must they? Feelings ought to be confined to me.

'I must go and pick the roses,' my mother said, aware that she was getting nowhere but hoping that her words would, like vaccination, take later. At lunch they had Sir Giles Gilbert Scott there, and were discussing the plans for the new Anglican Cathedral to be built in Cairo, and it was impossible to get a word in about white stockings, the irrationality of Rose Hunt, or anying else of moment.

Life seemed rapidly to be becoming complex and more difficult. I sometimes brooded over it now for as much as ten minutes at a time. It was bewildering in its demands. Even without Miss G., one could not, it appeared, freewheel happily along being oneself and letting other people accommodate themselves to it. Here one was, why could not other people just take it or leave it? Quite enough seemed prepared to take it, why must one bother about the ones that weren't?

The outer world was more complicated too. My father's face was more lined, we no longer went for walks together across the river and along the canals, padding along the dusty paths through the astonishing light and clarity of the landscape. The independence of Egypt was going far from smoothly. Allenby, having let the British Government have its fling in the form of the Milner Commission, had now taken matters into his own hands, and, backed by all the permanent English officials in Egypt, had been to England and startled the Cabinet into agreement with his plan to abolish the

Protectorate and declare Egypt an independent sovereign state. But there remained, alas, the thorny question of the Sudan, of defence, and of the Suez canal. Egypt being as it were at the cross-roads of the world, occupying a Piccadilly Circus site, was felt by the western nations to be vitally in need of stable government, only to be maintained by a standing British army. She could not be left alone as England had been, to have the Wars of the Roses in peace. Such was the view. That Victorian nightmare, the power vacuum, still haunted and would perhaps for ever haunt the western imagination. Needless to say, different dreams haunted the imagination of the Egyptians. They could hardly be expected to feel the same enthusiasm as Rose Hunt and I did for the continued presence of the British army, in spite of the handsome amount of money there was to be made out of them.

Even without these insoluble problems, this measure came too late. As ever, the British Government, moving deliberately and taking everything in turn with strict impartiality, had left things too long. As ever, the wise and moderate indigenous statesmen had been kept waiting, temporized with, until their people had lost faith in them. Saad Zaghloul, an able and disappointed politician, now embodied the national dream. Refusing to form a government himself or to allow anyone else to form one, or to meet anyone for consultation, he was steadily booking his ticket for the Seychelles, where he was presently sent. His admirers immediately put about the rumour that he was being tortured, and so the long sad enmity gathered force.

The singular system whereby the British imprison all those national leaders who have the vision and the imagination to lead, the necessary passion to carry them through their own divisions and hatreds into freedom and to withstand its early disillusionments, mysteriously works. Perhaps the authorities feel that this is the only way to make up to them for not having been to a public school. The imprisonment is clearly necessary because such qualities are nearly always combined with the dangerous power to rouse men to violence and bloodshed. Treated with kindness, freed from the necessity of earning a living, allowed ample reading matter and the leisure in which to imbibe it, separated from the intoxication of the crowds and the temptations of demagogy, safe from assassination by political rivals or failure through political error, they blossom into statesmen. It does not, however, feel like that at the receiving end at the time, and rarely is independence achieved without dust and heat, and a long legacy of bitter lies.

In wars and revolutions it is always the wrong people who are killed. It is not the leader, cosily eating Marie biscuits with his elevenses in the balmy climate of the Seychelles, thumbing through the *New Statesman* and the letters from his fans. The instigators, paid, duped, or merely makers of trouble for trouble's sake, are always safely at the back of the crowd. It is the ardent and idealistic young man in front, inflamed with noble dreams, whose lifeblood trickles out into the dust. Nor is it the delayer, thumbing through the files in the Colonial Office in England and leaving the matter over until after the holiday, who suffers. One of the first English victims of assassination in Egypt was an elderly official in the Ministry of Education, on the eve of retirement from a long career spent largely in trying to get better terms of service for Egyptian teachers. Another victim had just that day arrived in the country as doctor for an Egyptian hospital. Zaghloul had no direct responsibility for any of this, nor did it delay or hasten the transference of sovereignty. All that it sowed were the dragon's teeth of hatred and bitterness. As soon as a Prime Minister could be found to form a government and accept the new constitution, Zaghloul was brought back from the Seychelles and a general election was held which brought him into power. The British army stayed, a permanent thorn in the flesh of proud and politically conscious Egyptians, and there remained also that other more permanent Egyptian headache, Sudanese control of the headwaters of the Nile.

All this lived somewhere in the air this last winter, saddened the face of Mohammed, furrowed the brows of cab-drivers, caused even Rose Hunt sometimes to look nervously over her shoulder. I was occasionally aware of it, above and beyond my preoccupation with the coming parting. The break with child-hood was to be devastatingly complete, and this, in the midst of revelling in the last pleasures, I dimly understood. From now on I would see my mother only for two or three months in the year, my father only for one. William had stood it; and I hoped that I could: during the war he had not seen my father for four years. Such a separation seemed not quite real in prospect; improbably remote; not to be looked at very closely. But there were evenings when the night rustlings of the eucalyptus trees took on a requiem sound; everything was falling, dying, and autumnal; a searching sadness combed into my vitals. I would go out in the early mornings and look at my forest, already tall and prosperous, with a painful pride. Suppose it were to fail without my care, suppose the independent Egyptians were not to *want* it? The splendid saplings stood hopefully, their leaves moving almost imperceptibly in the crystal air. Nobody, surely, I told myself, could fail to want them.

At other times heaviness was far from me. There were wonderful desert picnics, on Fridays, the government holiday of the week, when we would ride out in large parties from Helouan into the rocky outskirts of the Mocattam Hills. Eastward the desert stretched away towards Sinai and Asia; its rocks and crags, its sand and stones and silent valleys laid their strong charm upon me. Riding in the sparkling air, eating sandwiches in the just-right February sun, one felt that anyone, that anything, might suddenly come round the edge of the barren cliff; a lion, roaring after its prey, Elijah and the ravens, Scheherezade in a veil, the last of the Mameloukes on a sweating horse, Ali Baba with his train of mules, or St John the Baptist. Actually it was generally one of my loved objects, having opened the beer. More deeply, the desert beguiled one with its own essence; with its silence, its emptiness, its strange and naked peace.

My father sat at breakfast in the dining-room. I had come down to ask him some necessary question about the ring round Saturn, was it solid or not? He could be trusted to know. He was eating yoghourt out of a small earthenware bowl, not for health reasons which had not then been thought of, but because it was a local dish and he liked it. The dining-room was immediately under the night nursery and they both faced north, for coolness sake. This morning it seemed rather dark. My forest was beginning to take effect outside it, but this was a thought I dismissed. Perhaps it was one of those rare days of winter when the Egyptian sky is clouded. The table was covered with the usual white damask table-cloth and there was a circular mahogany dumb waiter with marmalade and butter and sugar on it in the middle of it. This seemed scarcely necessary as Mohammed hovered in the background, wearing the habitual suffragi uniform of long white robe, red cummerbund, and red tarboosh on the head. For best he had a dark green silk one with gold on it. Dedicated to the retrograde proposition that a life spent ministering to the domestic wants of another man whom you admire and like is a life well spent, he lingered, a dark and amiable presence, by the coffee pot on the sideboard. I hope that when in due course he retired to his Nubian village, loaded with presents and riches and my father's frock coat and top-hat for wear on ceremonial occasions, he still felt the same. Probably; the Moslem proposition that we are all equal in the sight of God and that this vital status is unaffected by what job we do, was imprinted right through him, like the name of a seaside town through a stick of sugar rock. I also hope that the waters are not about to flood his honoured grave. He operated the electric toaster, not yet on the popping-up principle, shaped like a chest of drawers and of plated silver; chromium being still in the womb of time. There were reproductions of Dürer drawings on the walls. The lampshade hanging low over the middle of the table was of gathered dark green silk, as was also the curtain suspended from a brass rail along the back of the serpentine-fronted, lion-head-handled sideboard. On the floor was a salmon-red Turkey carpet, round the border of which we had what must have been a most irritating habit of leaping from medallion to medallion when let in towards the end of our parents' meals. My father was reading the *Egyptian Gazette* and did not look up. I came and swung, tiresomely, with one wrist on the table and one on the arm of his chair.

He put the paper down and began on his letters and I began on Saturn. His fingers were blunt-edged and stained with nicotine. I noticed suddenly that he was having difficulty in opening the envelope, and this gripped me without warning in a spasm of astonished pain. I underwent that strange unbearable wrench by which one's soul seems to be corkscrewed out of one's being and into someone else's, there to suffer for them a quantity of things which they are not even thinking of suffering for themselves. It was the very slight opening of a door which would never again shut quite so tightly, a door into a world where other people had existences of their own; where other people loved, felt, endured; were lonely, exultant, or bloody-minded, without reference to me. For one whose quickened imagination could focus only upon itself, this was a sharp blow in the solar plexus, an unprecelented heaving of the solid ground beneath the feet. Hitherto my father had existed only in this function, never as a person in his own right. That he could grow old, or diminish, or fail in any way had never entered into my conception of him. For the first time I saw him as a man like other men; subject to old age, feebleness, disaster, even death. An experience that was in the main sentimental, it was also briefly, revealing, even appalling; like a sudden fall which drained one of blood as one rushed through unfamiliar air. I sat down abruptly on a Chippendale chair and forgot the ring of Saturn. From the hall came the sound of the cuckoo clock striking half-past eight, and I remembered that I had failed to complete my homework, which was papering a room twenty feet by twelve, and the principal events of the reign of Louis Quatorze.

The last morning arrived, and was as heartlessly beautiful as ever. I dressed with an unforgetting, photographing eye fixed upon the pyramid of Cheops. My footfalls sounded sadly round the garden, even the squeak of the last swing had a melancholy fall. The leaves of the apricot grove glittered in the brilliance of the morning, datura flowers hung richly in their green gloom. Mohammed smiled as ever, the kindness of his pock-marked face was an ache against the heart.

The birds still sang as my new luggage was loaded at the gate. 'If you can manage not to cry,' my mother had said, 'it will make things easier for your father.' But would it be possible? In theory I was coming back, perhaps for some distant Christmas holidays, in spite of the ten days' journey from

England. In theory I was coming back, grown-up, to enjoy the sweets and splendours of adult Cairo life. In theory this was no goodbye. But children, like dogs, sometimes know things in their bones, and what my bones were saying this bright morning was goodbye for ever.

It was impossible to look back at the green-shuttered house, at the stone steps leading up to the front door with their pots of freesias and cinerarias and pelargoniums, at the stone gate-posts on whose broad tops Alethea and I had so often sat, two non-matching heraldic beasts. The road was spattered with bright sunlight and deep shadow, with the lozenge-shaped leaves of the leboc trees spreading out into the sun. The timeless Nile rolled under, the horses' hooves rang out again across the iron of the Boulac bridge. As the train drew out of Cairo station, leaving my father's grey-flannelled figure on the platform, leaving the comprehending faces of Mohammed and Suliman, I reached the end of this particular tether, and the fields of the Delta dissolved before my eyes. 'Well done,' my mother said, 'you lasted out.' I was pleased that she was pleased, but otherwise this victory seemed of little worth. From her corner Rose Hunt sniffed sympathetically; Alethea, glancing up from *Little Folks,* seemed to look faintly diverted. By Tanta I was deep in *The Viper of Milan,* and half-way through a box of Turkish Delight, and for once no one seemed concerned about my spoiling my lunch.

As we sat that evening on the dimly lit upper deck of the ship, my mother unaccountably decided that the moment had come for a sex talk. Perhaps, what with her social life, and the

Authorized Version, and the continued presence of Alethea in the night nursery, she had never before had an opportunity. I was twelve and a half; it seems strange that living in uninhibited Egypt, I had not got around to knowing the facts of life before. Her discourse, which in any case was halting, less from embarrassment than from a determination (unrealised) to make it all entirely clear, was interrupted by the arrival of the late train from Cairo, and by the consequent irruption on to the deck of a number of friends. Sent by their wives in search of bookable deck-chairs, they advanced smilingly, Colonel this and Sir Mortimer that; approaching from time to time with kindly expressions of pleasure at finding that our journey was to be made in company. In the intervals my mother pressed on with her task. The coming and going of all these stately fellows seemed to make the whole thing even more improbable than it sounded.

Could they have engaged in these droll and surprising gymnastics? Yet all, except Sir Ronald Storrs, were known to be fathers. I looked at them with goggle eyes.

In the background, across the dark waters of the harbour, the lights of Alexandria winked and flickered a sardonic accompaniment.

SLIGHTLY FOXED PAPERBACKS

Adrian Bell, *Corduroy*
Ysenda Maxtone Graham, *Mr Tibbits's Catholic School*
Diana Holman-Hunt, *My Grandmothers and I*
Michael Jenkins, *A House in Flanders*
Priscilla Napier, *A Late Beginner*
Rosemary Sutcliff, *Blue Remembered Hills*

Slightly Foxed Paperbacks are published by
Slightly Foxed Ltd. For more information please contact us at
53 Hoxton Square, London N1 6PB
tel 020 7033 0258 · fax 0870 1991245
all@foxedquarterly.com · www.foxedquarterly.com